Healthy Voice

Healthy Voice

LIFE BEYOND THE WEIGHT

MEREDITH TERPELUK

Healthy Voice: Life Beyond the Weight

ISBN: 978-0-9883867-0-9

Written by Meredith A. Terpeluk

Edited by Mary Diamond Stirewalt, Zorina Exie J. Frey and Michelle Singer

Cover and Interior Design by 1106 Design

Table of Contents

Dedication

This book is dedicated to my Dad who taught me how to live life to the fullest, love fully, have a positive attitude, and be passionate about my purpose in life.

A special shout-out goes to Mike, who stood by me through this entire writing process and to every person I've come across thus far who has led me to this point. It's dedicated to my family and friends and to all those who have shared their experience, strength, and hope. Thanks to Milestones in Recovery for getting me started on my journey. There is no way I would be here today without your courage. To the Healthy Voice Community, you know who you are—thanks for inspiring my Healthy Voice!

Finally, thank you God! If it weren't for you, I wouldn't have found this path. You are the creator of all the good in my life and you've given me this gift of the Healthy Voice to share with the world! May it shine in their hearts and may I always remember you are my main Healthy Voice.

An Introduction to Your Healthy Voice

My name is Meredith Terpeluk. You may not know my name. I hope by the end of my book though, you will know my story and most importantly, you will know your own path to your Healthy Voice.

If you've ever struggled with your weight, then you've probably struggled with an Unhealthy Voice telling you that you have to fix your body. If you've ever been on a diet, you've answered the call. Many of us need to lose weight for health reasons, but many of us have underlying root causes. These can't be healed with a quick fix. I spent over twenty years trying to do that with every possible external fix and none of them ever worked. What started with one event in childhood, my parents' divorce, which wasn't the cause of my problem but the trigger for it, ended up being the entry point for my addiction and an Unhealthy Voice starting with food to make its way into my life. That started me on the track of an unhealthy, emotional need for food, of feeling trapped in a body I didn't want to look at, and feeling I wasn't good enough because of my circumstances and my weight. I hated the weight so much I became addicted to losing it thru diets and marathons. Then the alcohol came into my life in college, and the weight packed on so fast I didn't know what to do. I knew at the time I may have the gene that runs in my family, but I just saw it as alcohol—never related the food, let alone any other behaviors. All of this time I was turning to the food, the diets, the marathons, the alcohol—the surface—I was avoiding what was going on beneath the surface. Focusing on the weight and fixing it was just deflecting me from the pain inside. Consequently, that's where I needed to go to grow.

It takes what it takes. I had to go down the road and I did. We all have our own roads. I had to be desperate enough to realize my willpower wasn't strong enough to change my circumstances. I had to be willing to get beyond the weight and go beneath the surface to find that I could change the road I was going down. This one had too many potholes that I was temporarily covering up with quick fixes. There had to be another way that would make the road of life less chaotic. I didn't know what that way was, but I knew it was better than this eventual crash I was headed towards. I wanted a better life and I was willing to do whatever it took to choose a different path. I was willing to get a new roadmap, read the directions, and follow the road signs that would take me to a better place than where I was.

This book is about my journey, how I changed direction, and how I live today. It's not the quick fix answer. It's about living life on life's terms when you've struggled with weight and you want to get beyond your crazy life that is focused on that alone. You want to live! I found that I just wanted to live with my eyes focused on the horizon with my feet planted on the ground, rather than with my eyes focused on the past trying to run from it. I found a power greater than me in a Higher Power and I found recovery from the crazy life I was living on the inside. I found that life is about a journey and not a fix. In order to live it that way, you've got to get tools instead of pretending there is a finish line coming. I was given this gift to share with you called the Healthy Voice that I hope you'll find to be something that serves as a light for you and a positive way to look at life rather than just your weight. I hope it gives you the courage to know yourself and the power greater than you. I hope it gives you the courage to separate yourself from something I call your Unhealthy Voice so you finally get to understand that it is not you. It's just been trying to convince you of that your whole life. The tough part is that it will always be whispering in your ear trying to throw you off track. The awesome part is that through this book, these tools, and the Healthy Voice Community, you'll begin to get strong in the face of it. Don't worry. We all have that voice of fear. Now you just get to let go of the one that tells you that your weight is your only self-worth and actually do something about it. That's a huge burden to be lifted!

I hope that this book will help you get to know your Healthy Voice and how it lifts your spirit, connects you to the spirit in others, inspires you, grounds you, and leads you on your path to joy and purpose. I hope you find its power within you and all around you. I hope you find that the meaning of healthy goes way beyond what society tells you and that the Healthy Voice goes right into what it means for you. Don't make it as small as eating healthy and working out. Let it guide you and empower you in every aspect of your life and see how much more there is to you than just being "healthy"! My real deep hope is that by reading my story, you will have the courage to recognize your own Healthy Voice so you can change. I wrote about where I was so that all of us who are stuck fixing the weight, knowing that we have to go deeper but don't know how, can finally start looking at what might lie beneath the surface. It's written so that you can meet yourself on the Healthy Voice journey and stop eating or dieting over your story. It's time to let it go and work through it so you can live! I hope you'll start to notice that it hasn't been about the weight, but all the ways the Unhealthy Voice tries to keep you distracted from what's beyond it. I hope you start to find out some of the "whys", not focus on blame, and get to know you better.

We all know how to "fix" our weight, but we all need to get beyond it. We all need tools for living when that 90-day program ends or when we can't even find the courage within to start. More importantly, we all need each other! It's time to put down the stick that tells us we are in this weight battle alone and that we have to compete with other people for results! No. It's time to stop sharing the simple before and after pictures. It's time to start sharing where we are right now, what got us started, what keeps us going, and what we struggle with as we walk! No one has got this down pat so we have to start sharing the journey honestly and stop keeping it on the surface! Yes, I'm here to break the rule in society that suggests you can't share your weight struggles and that you must focus on the pant size and scale. Let's stop focusing on that and get to the real stuff! Let's share our journeys because there is so much more strength in that! We all deserve to settle in for the life journey instead of tense up about the weight loss journey. Frankly, there are more interesting things to talk about—like how you are finding your Healthy Voice and how your Unhealthy Voice is trying to throw you off track! There is too much life to live to narrow it down to a scale every morning!

The Statistics

You may be someone who can't take your eyes off the obesity statistics. I've had the pleasure of studying them up close. In fact, I left my political job at the White House to pursue my passion for childhood obesity in the Secretary's office at the Department of Health and Human Services (HHS) right when the news media started to cover it in 2004. I thought I could be the voice for childhood obesity at the tables of power and influence. Yet what I found after two years of working there was that the power to change didn't lie in the hands of big government. The power lies right in you. So, I've seen the statistics. I keep up with the new ones. I've seen that one presentation from the Centers for Disease Control (CDC) that is used in so many leading experts' presentations to showcase how obesity has progressed over the years in our country. We all know how bad it has gotten.

These are the most recent statistics according to the Centers for Disease Control published in January 2012 for the year 2009-2010 based on the BMI factors for obesity:

- 35% of U.S. adults were obese.
- 16.9% of U.S. children and adolescents were obese.
- The prevalence was higher among adolescents than among preschool-aged children and higher among boys than girls.
- Over 78 million (more than one-third) U.S. adults and about 12.5 million (almost 17%) U.S. children and adolescents were obese.[1]

I see these and it's like a broken record. I almost dread when new ones come out because I know how the media is going to respond to it. I also know as a consumer who is affected by it and how the messaging is going to affect me. If I don't know my Healthy Voice, it's going to make me feel bad about my weight. If I'm someone who has never had the problem, it's probably going to make me judge those who do. It creates just as much division in our society as any political issue. Maybe if we give a little less power to the numbers and put more emphasis on the power within the individual to change their own circumstances (beyond the simple physical fix!), we may be able to shift those numbers. In the meantime, from my perspective—we're just going to keep doing the same thing over and over again expecting a different result. We're going to keep fighting it with activity and exercise alone, leaving the behaviors, the emotional responses, and the life after the weight fix up to the individual never giving them a roadmap. This is why I believe we're stuck in extremes.

The Extremes

We've got people that are on one end of the spectrum adding to the obesity statistics that often turn a deaf ear and keep eating because it's better than changing, or the idea of losing weight is like moving a mountain in their minds. We've got people that hear these statistics and get more obsessed with fixing their weight through diet and exercise. We've got people that discriminate against those people who "just can't lose the weight or stop eating." Then we've got the people who are trying to fix those who struggle with their weight by telling them they'll help them get the weight results they want. Without a Healthy Voice, the person will be taken down a road of thinking that the weight will fix all their problems. They go right towards the equal sign of physical activity and nutrition and risk missing so much! Many amazing solutions have been created to help people lose the weight but people need the ways to get beyond it to create lasting change too! Sometimes I just want to yell, "Stop! Don't go any further! Help them find their Healthy Voice first!"

This cycle we're in of fixing the problem on the surface alone is being handed down to the next generation. It's hard for them to find a Healthy Voice as whole selves when they are being told it's about not being obese. It's a whole other level of self-esteem issues in the bag! I'm all for giving kids healthier choices and getting them moving. I've been a huge promoter of that, but I'm a huge advocate for the hearts and minds since I realized that was my missing piece. Too many kids like me can't afford to skip the rest.

I realize this is a very forward way of thinking. That's mainly why I've written this book, so that those who read it can start to get a fresh perspective. To live it, you'll have to be courageous and willing to walk your own path rather than what everyone else is telling you about what to eat. I think you'll find not only peace in your mind and body, but empowerment from your deepest being. Not only that—I believe the more people that find their Healthy Voice, the more we'll be able to be present to those who seek it. The fear around weight, obsession with food and bodies—has got to stop. The insanity has gone too far and it's only going to lead to self-destruction with eating disorders and more obesity. I'm not saying don't work out, eat right, or get more research done—but let's get on our own journey with the Healthy Voice and out of the extremes! Yes, it will be weird to not participate in the conversations where friends are talking about dieting. It gets even weirder when someone tells you how thin you look. When someone tells me I look good and say, "You wrote a book on that? You had a problem?" Yes my friend. This is why I'm writing this book because this weight problem is not on the surface people! It's in our hearts and minds. It's in our bodies and it's weighing us down in more ways than the physical. In fact, at the deepest levels of our being—our souls are crying out for help. They want to know why we're letting the world tell us how to fill ourselves up in ways only a higher power can. They want to know why we've gotten so obsessed with our bodies and how we've lost balance so much. They are begging for some healing and attention because our souls know that is where the work lies. Our spirit is where the power lies. Contrary to popular belief, our most powerful piece is not in our bodies. It's on the inside of us. It's this light we've ignored because we've been too busy trying to gather it outside of us. We've got to shake off the dust and let our light shine!

What is at Stake?

There is so much more at stake than just our appearance as individuals and our countries. Our physical health is on the downside with all of the obesity related diseases on the rise in adults and children. Our mental health is virtually ignored. It took me close to twenty years to realize that my thinking and my brain chemistry was actually playing a role in my eating behaviors, weight, and lifestyle. That is too long. There needs to be greater consciousness about this. Not only that, many of us who are in unhealthy relationships with food struggle emotionally, yet we're convinced that the answer is purely eating right and working out. It's not so simple to be fixed through a magazine advice column. Some people have trauma they've gone through in their past that is manifesting itself through their relationship with food and weight. Until it's looked at, nothing will change—another reason we can't just look at the weight! So many of those people who struggle with trauma don't just have trouble with food. They are dealing with depression, anxiety, and eating disorders that they've been running from for years. They've manifested themselves through eating disorders like Exercise Bulimia, Binge Eating, and Orthorexia that go virtually unnoticed in our society.

Food addiction is a beast unto itself, directly related to the eating disorder but also related to a genetic predisposition meaning that just having a family that has unhealthy behaviors isn't the only issue. Not only that, it's not limited to food. Many people who suffer from the food addiction suffer from co-occurring disorders with other substances and behaviors. Throw in the idea that it can be treated with a diet or an Unhealthy Voice passed down through a family of "I'm fat and I need to diet," and you've got a trap where someone needs to break the cycle to prevent the next generation from going there too. This may be intergenerational but we can change our family trees. We can address more than just the obesity that is handed down. We can address the emotional issues before they fall apart and the mental issues that may impact the physical or behavioral. It's all connected! I see too many kids carrying way too much weight and I know with every fiber of my being that it's not about just the weight or their eating behaviors. I can see it in their eyes and understand where they've been. They deserve a better journey, a Healthy Voice one where they can make healthy voice choices for their whole selves and whole lives!

The Work of the Healthy Voice

I left my government job at Health and Human Services because I knew it wasn't where I was supposed to lead. I found out in my early days of eating disorder treatment that people were missing this huge piece of the puzzle and I wanted to help them find it. I just didn't know how yet. When I got out of treatment and got certified as a life coach, I named my company Core Wellness. People would come to me thinking I was a wellness coach that would finally give them the answers to their weight woes. They wanted me to tell them how to eat perfect, or lose that weight. I always said, "No, I don't really do that. I help you find your Healthy Voice." See, we've all got it within us to find that compass.

Yet, we've been so groomed to look at magazines, diets and quick fixes for the solution. It's not about the solution. It's about the way. It's about finding the things that work for us on the way in our lives. Life is not just a physical process, but a mental, emotional, and even spiritual one. We are spiritual and emotional beings, not just physical.

I have found in my work that the Healthy Voice speaks to every generation. College women who are trying to navigate the stress of school and also find out who they are, love it because it helps them find their positive voice for the path. When they get out of college, it's like the roadmap for the journey you never got. Women on a weight-loss journey love it because it finally gives them the relief in believing that their weight is not their only worth. It's like the big light bulb goes off! I love seeing the confidence rise in someone who realizes there is more to this life than weight loss. It's like, "I'm okay! Whoa!"

Right before I wrote this book, I was invited to be a part of something I never thought was possible in the world of weight-loss, let alone be invited to the table to help create a program. As a wellness consultant to the Employee Health Program at the Cleveland Clinic, I was able to be part of a project with Dr. Paul Terpeluk, DO and Medical Director of Employee Health Services (and uncle) and Gary Heavin, Founder and CEO at the time, of Curves International. Together we built a program called *Curves Complete,* the first of its kind, that included fitness, nutrition, and the final piece of behavior modification and motivation that I got to help create. Together we designed a curriculum and motivational scripts for videos that would inspire women to really think about the process of their lifestyle. It was an honor to not only have a seat at the table in the process, but to be a voice for these women. It was like all that time I was trying to get my voice heard at HHS didn't matter, because many women would be impacted with this right now. The impact we would make in coming together astounded me sometimes when we were creating it. It still does when I think about it. What amazes me even more is that the leader in this Gary Heavin wanted to give women a lifestyle. He was done with the relapse model of most diet programs. I couldn't believe I was hearing it, but I sure was grateful to God to be part of the process for these women.

Why the Healthy Voice?

With everything I've been exposed to at the national level around obesity, combined with my own struggle with my Unhealthy Voice, I have seen people everywhere, every day that are in the dark. I want to help bring the light. I want to be part of the shift from the Unhealthy Voice reaction in our society to a Healthy Voice collective response. The market is laden with fixes on the surface. People need a companion for the journey beneath the surface. Those that are stuck eating over the shame and fearful of weight need this. Those that are stuck with eating disorders or food addictions leading their life need a Healthy Voice to guide them out of it. Those on the weight-loss journey looking for something beyond it could use this guide to help them maintain it for life. Those parents who have kids that struggle with food, weight, or eating disorders could become more aware of what that struggle might look like. Those stuck in extremes that want to get out, might find hope for a Healthy Voice instead. It doesn't matter where you are. It just matters where you are willing to change. It's from that place that you can begin to change—whether it's physically, mentally, emotionally, or spiritually.

If you don't think you've got it, think about what you've already gotten through or done in your life—and you'll realize you've got it in you. I don't have to sit across from you while you read this to know you've got the light within you. Now it's just time to tap into it. You deserve it. If each of us taps into this, I truly believe it will empower the world one person at a time. Little by little, those statistics could change if we seek to address them in our own lives by going beyond the weight.

I don't know about you, but I'm done being distracted by the Unhealthy Voice. I'm done focusing on the surface. I'm done fixing the outward problem alone. I'm walking beneath the surface and meeting myself. I'm meeting you if you are willing to go to that place beyond the weight. I'm done looking at weight as the problem. I know that it's the result of underlying problems that need to be worked through in a person's life—not in a day, or a diet, but often through the journey of a lifetime! I'm ready to help you get to that life beyond the weight.

Your Invitation to the Healthy Voice Community

There is a Healthy Voice Community of people that have already started walking the journey in their own way. They get it, in their own way and I want you to join us. We all have our stories and a way we got to our change. Not all of us got to it through a physical change or weight-loss. Yet all of us have found our Healthy Voice in our own way. We recognize there is a light inside of us and we're part of a group that chooses not to sign up for society's labels telling us our worth lies in our weight. We haven't got life all figured out. We just realize that life is a lot more than weight-loss. We don't let society define us. We let a power greater than us do that and we let it empower our lives. We're on the path—learning, growing, leading, and becoming the people we are meant to be. We don't focus on the before and after shots. We focus on how we got there, what it took, and what keeps us strong. We share our stories and what inspires us so we can inspire you. This is bigger than us, and we know it. We know this is for you.

This book and the journey it entails will help you meet yourself where you are at, without having to fix yourself every time you struggle. You will transform in ways you never knew you could, just because you are willing to change whenever and wherever you are ready to do it, and you will do it again and again. Losing the next pound won't be anywhere as cool as the revelations you'll find on this path.

I hope that whatever God does with this book in your life and in the lives of all those it touches, will be a beacon of life, a channel for peace and a tool for transformation. I'm excited to see what lies ahead on the journey. I hope you'll join me because I know from my perspective that it's time for you to see the light I know is in you! It's time for you to be freed of that chain telling you that the weight is it! You got a life beyond the weight to live, my friend. If I could find a way, you can find a way right to that light in you.

There is one more thing I want you to remember as you read this. I didn't write this because "I got this." I wrote it because I needed to share my story just as much as you need to and I need these tools for living just as much as you need them. I don't have all the answers. I'll be learning until the day I leave this earth! All I know is I'm focused on the horizon, with my feet planted firmly on the ground. So, let's get started—together!

PART I:
Early Childhood

CHAPTER ONE:

The Beginning of my Relationship with my Unhealthy Voice

Elementary School and my Parents Divorce

I had this revelation when I was 34 and went through a tragic loss: "I was a pretty happy kid. I just had an Unhealthy Voice that tried to tell me I wasn't."

Dealing with my parents' divorce, carrying a family gene I didn't know about, and finding comfort in food. This is where I was in elementary school.

I know now that my genetic predisposition to my addiction was triggered by several factors but what set it in motion was my reaction to my parents' divorce. It is so hard to describe how truly traumatic divorce can be for kids. No matter how "good" the divorce can be in the parents' eyes, it's still a trauma, it is a major loss that merits a process of grieving for all involved. Today, it has become so commonplace that it seems it has almost lost its "shock value". Kids and parents often struggle to get through it emotionally and turn to food like I did. Many struggle spiritually in believing they aren't good enough for God because of the stigma around it in the church. Many others feel intense judgment from society, like they wear a Scarlett Letter of sorts similar to the weight. To me, they are no different. The reality is that so many people go through this—apparently close to 50% of the population—and it's those people that need hope of letting go of the shame and fear that they aren't loved. These are the people who can be guided through to healing with light and love. Everyone deserves that, to get beneath the surface to the issues—whether it's the weight or divorce. To me, that is more powerful for changing the generational impact of divorce than any repeated announcing of statistics or judgment around it.

I know at age 7, I was shocked. My world went upside-down. I was going to split my time between two parents, two households, two lives, two different souls. Little did I know how much that experience would have the ability to affect every facet of my life in both positive and negative ways, but I had to navigate my way through my Unhealthy and Healthy Voice with it. You'll learn more about it in my next book.

My Mom's world and Dad's world were very different, as were their outlooks on life. They marched to the beat of their own drummer. It used to feel like Mom and I were going through the motions every day trying to make the most of it and Dad would take me to fantasy land in Washington D.C. every other weekend. It was literally two different worlds and three hours apart. Each time, as I was shifting from one household to another, I subconsciously thought to myself, "How do I fit in here? Who do I need to be here to make mom happy? Who do I need to be here to make Dad happy?"

At the end of the day, wherever I was, I would feel bad if I was not being the person I thought my Mom or my Dad wanted me to be. If I wasn't being the best of the best for Dad, I felt bad. If I was being too much like my Dad, I felt bad around Mom. Mom was taking care of me as best she could and had to find her own coping devices through the divorce. Those seemed to be working a lot (which she didn't love), running and praying a lot. I knew she was in a lot of pain and I hated myself for not being able to fix that. That is a big job for someone who wasn't even 10 yet. At the same time, I was watching Dad start a new life in D.C. with a new career in politics and a new girlfriend. Things were changing quickly.

The woman he was dating was named Diane and of course as a child, an only child, who'd just lost her Dad, it felt like she was going to be my replacement. I felt like I'd lost him to her. Little did I know that when I first met her, she would become this Healthy Voice for me, this champion for my Healthy Voice in staying grounded in my truth, in trusting myself and the spirit of Dad within me to carry me. I didn't know any of this the day I met her. She had given us a tour of the West Wing and greeted us in the Old Executive Office Building. All I remember was her walking ahead of me and Dad asking me what I thought, but I was too young to comprehend what was going on in his heart. Then, sometime after that and a few times getting to know each other, Dad told me on a Friday night drive to D.C. that he'd asked her to marry her. I just about lost it. I wanted to jump out of the car. My Unhealthy Voice jumped out from within me in sheer terror. It wasn't something I could change. I was just a kid who didn't know how to react. What I didn't know was that on an even deeper level, this would be the beginning of a marriage that would give me the hope that I could be married. Even though they were three hours away much of the time, the time we spent together in D.C., in South Bend, on trips to California, and overseas would show me what two people who truly love each other can do to make a marriage work and to create a family. I didn't know it then, but they were lighting the way for my future marriage. Diane has truly been a huge blessing in my life on so many levels I still have yet to even comprehend. I'm just glad time and recovery has shown me how Dad and Diane were being a true beacon of light in coming together.

I didn't know that peace yet at the time. I felt overwhelmed by what was happening in life. I did not know where to turn. I did not know where to find solace. One of my most vivid memories, at the time, was going to my cousin's house nearby after school, the Andersons, an intact loving family living under one roof, where people sat around the table to eat meals together. I would soak in the smell of dinner and brownies, which gave me a sense comfort in a "normal" home. I can close my eyes and feel the comfort wave over me. I can smell those brownies.

Food had become the drug of choice for me, and the quickest, easiest fix for my feelings. It was the one thing I felt understood me, even though it wasn't a person. It could make me feel loved. It was my one friend that could get me through anything and would not judge me, leave me, or try to tell me to stop feeling. Everywhere I went when I saw food, I knew I could find solace in it. It helped me control my feelings. It also gave me a sense of control when I could not control events around me. It was my only sense of feeling grounded in between my two worlds. It was also the method I even used to manipulate my relationships with my parents. I tried to demand they show me love by taking me out to dinner. It was my measuring stick to gauge whether or not they loved me. Of course, their love was never predicated on this; I was just convinced it was. It was killing me slowly on the inside. It was killing our relationships yet I didn't know it. I thought I was controlling the pain by controlling the food. Years later I learned it had me under control. Food was the only thing I could turn to for the pain. Instead of turning to a sibling, as an only child, I turned to sugar fixes. I had no idea that I was isolating in my relationship with it. It was food, after all. How could that be? I was a kid! I was trying to suppress the pain and act like everything was fine.

I found out later an intense story how much power I was really giving to food. My cousin Jessica brought back a memory highlighting how powerful it had become in my life at an early age. Years later, she was not surprised at all when I eventually went to treatment for food addiction.

"Do you remember when we were in Brigantine and you yelled at us for eating the cake?" Jessica said.

I said, "What? I don't remember this." (That selective memory again.)

She said, "It was right after your parents got divorced. We were in the kitchen. Bacie (Polish for grandmother) had bought that Entenmann's lemon cheese danish with chocolate drizzled on top and told us not to eat it, that it was for breakfast. But Julie (her sister) and I went to take a bite anyway and you went crazy on us."

"What?" I asked.

She said, "Yes, you yelled us," and said, 'If there is anyone that, deserves that it's me because of what I'm going through with my parents' divorce."

When she told me this story, I could feel the anger again I had felt at that traumatic time. I always felt like I had to choose between my parents—which house to stay at, which parent should I talk to you about this, which parent should I lean on? Whichever one I would choose for whatever circumstance would be wrong because it would hurt the other. It was a horrible torment during this time as I loved them both so much. I just wanted to be accepted but it felt like I was a rubber band being pulled in two directions. They of course loved me immensely but because of my feelings, I felt ungrounded.

Addiction seemed to run in the family on both sides of the gene pool. Mom showed me through pictures when I went to treatment how her Mom had struggled with food herself and where she used to hide it. I knew Dad knew the addiction to alcohol on his side all too well. Even though I often wished he would just call me out my addiction when I was in it, I knew he was the one I was meant to call when I was ready be honest about it. He had been through it with someone else he loved and he understood. I thank God for the recovery on his side of the family because it brought me to a deeper understanding of the disease and out of the darkness. But even through the recovery journey, it's been a miracle to discover with both of my parents how our behaviors with foods have been addictive whether it's sugar or carbohydrates or even a behavior like shopping. Having those conversations helped us to understand each other I think.

My road to my Healthy Voice wouldn't start though until I got off the train towards my addiction. Until I did that, genetics would continue to load the gun where environments would pull the trigger. When I finally stopped it in its tracks, I learned where my pain originated. Looking back, it was easy to see it was the divorce, and how, at that point, I started to habitually rely on food to relieve my pain. It is important to recognize the difference. Once I learned where the pain originated, I needed to take the steps to remove the blame and shame from it, which I'd been doing for so many years. That's what kept me in my addictions. I also looked to my family for answers in our shared history. I started to assess my parents' day-to-day habits and choices in terms of exercise and food. We already knew addiction was part of our family history in both the alcohol and the sugar. My Dad loved sugar. He would devour loaves of bread, muffins or Tasty Cakes. All he ever wanted was carbohydrates and sweets (unless he was on a diet). I would see him going into the kitchen and diving into a pint of ice cream, sneaking around the corner at the store to get something at the bakery or at the ice cream shop at the beach. Mom was similar. She ate chocolate and gummy bears as a steady diet. We would go to the mall so she could go to the candy store and get the right ones or the special chocolate store to get the "good" chocolate. Apparently, I never really cared for it as a kid but as I got older I grew to love it, maybe because I saw what it was doing for her and wanted some for myself. As a kid, I was focused on "more". I just wanted bigger portions, Mom and Dad to give me more on my plate because that meant more love. Then you add in the sugar. Mom would have it in the car all the time and it's all I could think about but she wouldn't gain weight because she ran so much. My Dad, on the other hand, knew when he had too much at times and would go on a diet to drop all the weight he'd gained being in his favorite sugar and carbohydrates for a time. So they both had their own ways of managing the weight that came on with their love of sugar, which showed me that I could do a combination of both the dieting and the running! Yet, it hadn't registered yet that both of them were things I was doing more to just keep them happy rather than manage my weight.

Food remained my constant friend as I continued to navigate my life in between two worlds. Now, it had really started to show. My weight gain was obvious. I was getting more insecure about it. Consequently, I learned how to become a master of camouflage both emotionally and physically. These techniques would stay with me for many years. My Unhealthy Voice was screaming at me. Nothing I did was right.

I tried to cover my stomach up with huge button down men's shirts and elastic waistband shorts. I would not be caught dead in jeans. Around the water, I would not wear anything but a one-piece bathing suit with a tee shirt to cover my stretch marks. I hated sitting down. The rolls in my stomach would fold over. I was uncomfortable in my body. This only added to my insecurity of my parents being newly divorced and thinking all my friends thought there was something wrong with me for that reason. I was completely self-conscious. The worst part was that the one thing I thought I had under control, food, had clearly gotten out of control. I felt violated. The pattern had been set though. Eating would make it better. This is the chaos of food addiction. You keep doing it even though you do not want to but the problem is that eating is the only way you know to deal with your feelings. I was angry at the food, the weight, and my parents for doing this to me—whatever it was. I thought I had this whole thing under control. Yet the weight gain was like a flashing neon billboard, a blaring, glaring sign that I was screwing up. I was so ashamed. I could not stand to show myself to the world or to my parents. I thought my Dad would hate me like this and he would reject me 'more' now. The shame voice was really, really loud. So to get rid of it all, the emotional pain and the physical weight, we did what we only knew to do, we put me on my first diet around the age of eight.

I had mixed feelings about it. Although I wanted to look and feel better, I did not want to lose the one friend in food I had that I knew for sure would never leave me. Now, it would be taken from me? My

Unhealthy Voice ™, the one I didn't even know I had at the time, did not like that. I did hate the way I looked more than I loved food though, so I was willing to sacrifice my love of food for better self-esteem with a diet. I was angry at the food. I felt abused by this one-way relationship. I wanted out of it even though I was the one who signed up for in the first place.

I became excited about finally losing the weight! I would be accepted. I would not turn to food for every feeling. Little did I know that by taking this next step, we would only be treating the symptom, not the disease, but we didn't know. I would start a vicious cycle of using the diet the same way I would use food, as a feelings and body fix. Anything to fix how I felt about myself! I do not remember the specifics of the first diet. I remember the strip malls I'd go to for weigh-ins at Nutri-System, Jenny Craig, and re-joining every time I gained. I remember my mother taking me to a Weight Watchers meeting in the back of Macy's at the mall, or Jenny-Craig weigh-ins and meetings. I had spent a lot of time at these centers even before I had gotten to high school. Diet centers became my after school sport. I remember wondering why I had to go through something like this, this punishment, just because I carried this weight. However, I also felt so accomplished when I lost weight. The highs and lows are ingrained in my memory. The euphoria of losing the weight, maintaining the number, and the look of joy from my parents! I'd finally made them proud because I was skinny! I truly thought the only way my parents would love me is if I lost the weight. This afterschool "sport" also gave me an opportunity to excel when my grades were underwhelming. My benchmark for success was now weight loss. It was not grades, hobbies, or having friends. The scale was my happiness meter. It gave me something else to focus on besides my two parental worlds and my poor grades. Losing the weight would mean I would look good on the outside. I would be a winner. Who does not like a winner? It was the key to success and it would negate all my shortcomings. Little did my mom, Dad and I know that this would be the beginning of us trying to "fix" the problem on the surface, instead of getting to the solution beneath it for a long, long time.

The Healthy Voice Makes an Appearance

As I was cruising along on this path, there were actually times when I did enjoy something other than the number dropping in the scale. I had the privilege of taking voice lessons and going to horseback riding camp every summer. Those were two things that would really spark the Healthy Voice inside me beyond just being healthy and I'm grateful to my parents for giving me those opportunities. Every voice recital I did in front of a hundred parents in the gym is the earliest time I can remember finding the confidence within me to use my voice. Every summer I'd ride at Gwynn Meadows Farm, I'd live for my time with the horses. While writing this book I was able to ride a horse again and think back to what it was like back then, how much that experience taught me responsibility. It also taught me to be proud and stand tall within my own Healthy Voice! How funny it is now to think about how much those two activities really helped carry me through that time, and they had absolutely nothing to do with a diet. Thank God!

The Diet Distraction

But of course, then I'd see a picture of myself in my camp clothes or in my recital dress and that moment of forgetting about my weight was gone. I hated pictures of myself. I hated having to buy the biggest dress size and I was completely embarrassed to wear a size-16 graduation dress from the 8th grade. Yet, when I could sing *Wind Beneath my Wings* at graduation I forgot about the size of my dress again. It still amazes me how much I let my obsession with my body block me from joy as a child.

Dieting was keeping me distracted from my emotional issues. So it makes sense to recognize how much I let my weight block me, because I didn't want to feel all the feelings I needed to feel! This is why I would always eventually go back to the food and then gain the weight again.

I was addicted to food to cope with my feelings. Nothing was going to change that course until I would intercept it. Diets were giving me a way to continue my addiction and manipulate it. As good as I felt on the outside, I still felt depressed on the inside. I felt like I was not enough. If I kept this weight off, I would be accepted is truly what I believed. This is when I started to believe, as a young kid, I had to maintain this facade to cover up what was going on inside. The dieting was the method I used to keep the food 'under control'. So, I had two control mechanisms going on—the food and the diets. The food gave me comfort. The diets gave me a self-esteem panacea as well as a body that showed I was doing "a-okay". I was not addressing the disease. But again, like much of the world—I wasn't seeing past my willpower as the problem.

I did need structure with my food. I was at an unhealthy weight. More importantly, I needed to address my feelings and not 'control' them with a diet or comfort emotional eating behind closed doors. I had no control. Consequently, I started to give power to everyone outside of me so they could tell me whether or not they thought I had it all under control. That is when I really started to depend on the scale and unfortunately, when I really started to depend too much on my Dad, or even complete strangers, for my self-worth. The women who weighed me at the diet offices were the arbiter of my self-worth that week and I'd go in there thinking I wouldn't survive if she gave me a bad face. What a nightmare. I was a kid in a dependent love affair with the diet and the scale. The number was not the problem though. My self-worth was the problem. I was not finding any worth inside myself. In fact I had no idea it was there. I was reaching for it externally and not internally. The reflection in my Dad's eyes, for example, was like a traffic signal which would determine the direction of my self-esteem. Splitting my time between two households, I would show up at his house in Washington, D.C. As soon as I went in the door, I would do an immediate read of his eyes to determine whether or not he thought I looked fat and if he did all guns were blazing. I mistakenly thought he would not love me unless I was losing weight (he was the first of many men, I would burden with this assignment). What little credit I gave my loving and supportive father whose face lit up whenever I came to see him no matter what because he just loved me unconditionally. Again, I didn't believe it. Any concern there may have been was only due to his concern for my health; not my looks, not the number on the scale. I could not see this though with my raging insecurities and method of 'controlling' what had now become a see-sawing weight gain and weight loss. Whenever I would visit him again, or the diet office, I always left with a feeling of failure if I could not just get the diet right. This went on for years and years. Now, I know it was never about me having the power to keep the weight off. It was about so much more.

At the time, my parents and I did not know that and we did not think to look within. Looking in from the outside, I was a generally happy kid, and by this point, I had learned to camouflage well. Of course, at some points, we tried therapy. These cursory attempts were always unsuccessful as I would hide the problem. Plus, I had a solution, of course! I kept declaring, "This time I'm finally going to get the weight off." I was like an alcoholic promising their loved one that they will quit the drink.

Regretfully, I realize now, during the diet phase, I made a hurtful mistake many times when I made Dad my food police. In reality, because of my dieting paired with his own struggle in his relationship with food and diets, we were in it together. Thankfully we would work through it. Yet, anytime we were in the presence of food that was not on my diet, or I was in a weight-gain cycle, he would 'helpfully' admonish, "You don't need that," or brush my hand away from food I wanted. I would be so angry with him and myself for the roles we took during this time. I've come to know his desire was solely to protect me from the pain he could see I was feeling. He thought protecting me from the food was protecting me from pain. He could not keep me from that food anymore than someone who loves an alcoholic can keep them from picking up a drink if they want it. No one can. My Dad was so important to me. Over the years, I ran to him for comfort for a skinned knee or a bad grade and many financial rescues. He always helped. He could not help me here. This problem was beyond both of us. He was the perfect person though to understand my issue with sugar. He struggled with it himself although not as seriously. He knew when he was on a yo-yo diet or looking from a high from sugar. If he could help me, it would save me from some of the choices he had made when he was younger. He did what he could to help me. We had no idea that even if there was a lower number on the scale, weight loss was only putting a band-aid on the real problem.

Let me tell you about the moment we realized it wasn't about the diet. We called it "the diet revelation talk". We had it when I was in treatment. He apologized profusely, "Mere, I am SO sorry!" and I said, "Dad! It's okay. We didn't know! Diets were all we knew!" We laughed and cried together and I said, "Can you believe this? Imagine how many parents out there are treating their kids with diets?" I felt so energized to go out and tell every parent not to do it. Not just because diets did not work for me but it hurt our relationship for a long time. I connected diet and weight loss with his love for me. One was dependent on the other. That was never his intention. He just wanted me to be healthy and happy, to not be hurting, to answer the call for help when he got it. My Dad did not know, of course, treating what he saw only on the surface would become damaging. The world seemed to be telling us to deal with the weight, the numbers! Get the scale! I believe, today, this still holds true and sets up more kids for the same extremes. I find it fascinating we are still debating whether or not to put kids on diets when there is clearly a larger issue at hand.

According to the National Association of Anorexia Nervosa and Associated Disorders (ANAD) website, over one-half of teenage girls and nearly one-third of teenage boys use unhealthy weight control behaviors such as skipping meals, fasting, smoking cigarettes, vomiting and taking laxatives. Forty seven percent of girls in 5th-12th grade reported wanting to lose weight because of magazine pictures. Sixty-nine percent of girls in 5th-12th grade reported that magazine pictures influenced their idea of a perfect body shape. Forty-two percent of 1st-3rd grade girls want to be thinner! The most staggering but realistic statistic one to me was the 81% of 10-year-olds are afraid of being fat.[2] Don't stop here. You saw the statistics in the beginning of the book about childhood obesity. According to the Obesity Action Coalition website, in a recent national survey of overweight sixth-graders, 24% of the boys and 30% of the girls experienced daily teasing, bullying, or rejection because of their size.[3]

Dieting will not address this epidemic issue until parents and kids are aware of the whole picture around them. I know through my experience that is no small feat. It means changing the conversation on the national level. The day I realized my parents did not have the answer, nor did I, was overwhelming. Diets, therapy, weight centers, food police; none of it was working for me. It doesn't mean it doesn't work for anyone but there are a lot of people who need to get off the train they've been on and get the real help they need to get beyond it. For me, I needed a new direction. I needed a higher power but it would be a long time until I'd come to find that on a deeper level even though He was with me all along.

It was then that I started to revisit my relationship with God, but it was one of anger. I just did not understand. I thought it was bad enough God took away my Dad in the divorce and now this ongoing weight struggle. When I could not see the light, I started asking questions, "Why me? Why such a battle? Why do I have to work so hard to be good enough God?" I felt powerless and in dark place. All I envisioned was a judgmental god who was up there with a rule book or a calorie counter telling me, "Keep going Meredith. Once you hit that perfect weight, then I'll love you but you aren't here yet." It was so not true! I could not hear what God is always saying,

I love you more than you will ever no or be able to grasp. I've loved you from the deepest fiber of your being since way before you were born and

I always will. No matter what you go through, I am with you, even when you can't see me. My love for you never has been or will be based on what you do or your circumstances out of your control. My love for you just is . . . .

It was an awakening moment for me years later, when I had what some call my spiritual awakening where I realized he was saying something like this. I had to recognize that he was up there, but he was down here right in my heart, but I wasn't there yet. I was just getting started with high school.

CHAPTER TWO:

Being a Teenager with my Unhealthy Voice in High School

I have a picture of my high school graduation that I keep on my desk. I often look at it as I am writing.

I call it "My Two Angels." I am dressed in a white gown holding a big bouquet of flowers standing in between two of my favorite people, my Dad and his Mom, my Grandmom Cass. I look like your average high school student happy on graduation day. I can look at that picture and remember how loud that Unhealthy Voice was in my mind though, and I did not even realize it. I used to look at this picture and think I looked fat. Now, I love it. It reminds me of where I was in my life and two of the special angels who are watching over me now. It also helps me have compassion for my younger, high school self.

The Fear of Rejection Continues

I started day one of high school feeling confident. I felt ready. Why? I had just lost a lot of weight on a pre-high school diet. I thought I had finally arrived. I thought because I "looked" healthy, I "got this" but my emotional, mental, and spiritual health was weak and I didn't know it. All I knew was that I was starting high school skinny and I was happy.

Consequently starting off like that set the bar for the scale as the self-worth barometer for any setback I would have in high school and even beyond. As long as I was dieting, that would be the case. My self-esteem would be up if the scale was down, or my self-esteem would be down if the scale was up. My worth was not determined by God's love for me, but by a piece of plastic on the bathroom floor. It made me feel very alone and defeated. That made my eating continue. Drinking started to show up as well, but didn't have much of an impact except I noticed a rash all over my neck and face. The early signs of an allergy I can see now.

High school is a tough new beginning. We all have fear of being rejected by our peers. It's a healthy fear. Then there are some of us who have a bunch of other stuff going on we don't know about or know how to cope and so we keep quiet or overcompensate with perfectionist qualities. I didn't know quite how loud my Unhealthy Voice was but I was certainly still reacting to it. I was thinking in my head that I was this victim of my parents' divorce and the weight struggle. I thought I got this raw deal. My Unhealthy Voice was shining bright and trying to keep me focused on finding my self-worth outside of me instead of within me. I could not appreciate the experience of high school. I was focused on what I did not have. When I did not get what I wanted I reacted with anger, seeking solace from food and rejecting myself even more. If it wasn't food, it was more diets. I wanted to be popular. I was comparing myself to girls in my class, angry at my peers, the girls I grew up with, who were now popular and feeling rejected by the 'in" crowd. Somehow though I was happy at times. I remember the joy I had with my friends, yet I remember this underlying Unhealthy Voice that I couldn't identify.

That Unhealthy Voice had me in its rapture. It was focusing on signs that I was being rejected. I was focused on boys who showed no interest in me and who did not ask me to the dance. I blamed myself for being fat and ugly. I also blamed my parents for even the possibility of rejection. If my Dad rejected me, it makes sense they would, too.

I would say to my friend with resentment, "Why? It's because of my weight isn't it? It is. If it wasn't that it was, "It's because my parents are divorced isn't it? It is."

Little did I know it was because I was showing such desperation and seeking validation outside of me not from within me. What high school boy would want to try and solve those problems? I felt like such an outcast. I went all through high school without a boyfriend or even having kissed a boy. I was very social though and that increased my confusion. I did not understand why all these boys we hung out with on the weekends did not like me. All I could do was beat myself up. Then, I was saying, "God, why won't you let a boy like me? What did I do now to deserve this?" Again, my outlet was to become angry with God, with my Mom and Dad. I wanted a boyfriend so bad and had this intense fear that I would never get one because of my circumstances and rejection as a child of divorce and the weight. Looking back now, there is beauty in the fact that the boys who didn't like me caused me to make my Dad that one guy for that much longer and make that many more memories visiting him in D.C. God always knows what He's doing if we just trust Him. He even gave me two incredible gifts during high school. They show me He's with me all the way, until this day.

As I was navigating these issues, college preparation time came around. I was absolutely terrified of a deeper rejection by my Dad. This time it was fear that I would never get into the dream school he wanted for me, Notre Dame. The time had finally come for me to apply to the school we had visited every fall with my stepmother's family. I knew it was going to be tough to be accepted. The day had always seemed so far off though and now it was here. I wanted to hide. My grades would never measure up and yet Dad was dying for me to get in there. The Unhealthy Voice was packing a powerful punch with this one. It said, *"Your grades are horrible. You will never be able to do it. Look at the other girls who are applying. They are the smartest of the class and you don't even rank. No way. You'll never be able to reach this goal."*

It was like all those times I wanted to make him happy by getting to a goal weight. He was such a supportive Healthy Voice for me through it all, "You can do this Meredith! I know you can," so was my stepmom Diane. Now it was something that felt far more insurmountable. As a team, we did everything in our power to make it happen. I worked really hard. Although I was not an academic, I still felt the need to compete with girls who had already been accepted. I wanted it and I was going for it. Even though I disliked it when I was a kid, I had grown to love the place. My Dad loved it so much, as did my stepmother. I had created a space for it in my own heart.

So, I took a SAT preparation class, focused on my application, and directed positive energy towards this goal. I wrote about a movie called "The Power of One" for my application. It was about a young boy named P.K. who grew up in South Africa during the apartheid.

Despite our efforts, I was rejected. However, if I worked hard enough and went to summer school, there was a chance I could reapply. So, as a family team, that is what we were going to do. We had a plan. Dad kept me on task. Of course my Unhealthy Voice ™ was going, *"You idiot. I knew you could not get in. First the weight, now this?"* Although I could not say it at the time, I was relieved to be enrolled in Gettysburg College that fall. It was a place close to both of my parents. Now, for the first time in my life, I felt settled in between my two worlds and appreciated the space to grow on my own. But I was also going to have to get ready to go to Notre Dame so I couldn't get too comfortable. It's the way I lived, between two worlds, always preparing for the next turn or change, never being able to just settle into myself.

How God was Taking Care of Me

God was taking care of me through all of high school. I just could not see it. I was too busy listening to my glass half-empty Unhealthy Voice, focusing on what I did not have. I had so many great things. I had great friends, a fun social life, and extracurricular activities, which were raising my spirit. I started building on what I started in grade school with my singing and got involved in all the groups after school at Gwynedd which I loved. I also was chosen by my teachers to represent my school in leadership events in Washington, D.C. and overseas. This made me realize there was a future beyond the classroom! What an exciting time.

My Unhealthy Voice was shouting at me though and I was comparing myself to all the other girls even with all of these good things happening. My Unhealthy Voice wanted me to be the best at everything, the soloist instead of member of the choir, the Valedictorian instead of middle-of-the-road student, the most attractive girl, and the one who got the boys. It wouldn't let me meet myself where I was at, ever. It wanted me to have everything I did not have, and to reinforce the notion I was never enough. Nothing was ever enough for the Unhealthy Voice. Consequently, I thought I needed to have more and something 'outside of me' would make me "enough." I was absolutely more than enough, I know now, and I had everything I needed right where I was at any moment.

For a long time I feared that I would be abandoned like I was as a child, like many children of divorce. Then I was given these two experiences where God showed me how much bigger His love was than my fear. I didn't realize the power at the time, but many years later I now do. The first was a trip in high school, with my Mom to Arizona. I was overtaken by the majesty and magnitude of the Grand Canyon and Sedona. I saw His wonder in Mother Nature and realized I would never be alone again. It was amazing to me at the time, but I realize now in my great love of nature around my Healthy Voice, that is when God really planted the seed of my love for nature. God is bigger than anything I could ever imagine. He is everywhere. Through that beauty of the Grand Canyon He truly showed me that everything is going to be all right. My recovery started right there, right then, I just did not know it and I'm grateful to this day for that trip with my Mom.

The other experience came on graduation day. As a child of divorce, if your parents don't communicate much, you fear the big days in your life like graduation and wedding. So I was terrified for this one. It had given me tremendous anxiety. Yet, God's grace arrived and I found out that my Mom has saved Dad and Diane seats for the ceremony. I cried and felt this sense of God's love overwhelm me, like I'd gotten a break for the special day.

Right after that day, I got another gift. Still a bit immature at the time, I wanted something material for my special day, but I got something even more special. Dad and Diane shared the news through a sonogram photo that I was going to have a sibling! For a split second I wanted to be the only child and take the news not well, but God took my heart and made it full of love and I'm so glad he did. Today, I have a little brother named Trey with my Dad's bright blue eyes, just like me. He is growing up to be an awesome kid. I am so grateful to have him in my life. Every single time I see him; I cannot help but see my Dad's spirit in him. It is such a gift for our family to share. We live far away now. Every time we see each other we hug as if we have never been apart. I cannot wait to see where this life takes him.

The Need So Many High School Students Have for a Healthy Voice

I tap into these high school experiences to help the high school age girls I have in my life now get through the transitions they experience. Whether it's the girls in my own home or ones I work with through a Healthy Voice program, I see firsthand the pressure these girls experience. Recently, I was given the opportunity to spend some time with some young girls from my high school, Gwynedd Mercy Academy in Gwynedd Valley, Pennsylvania. The Alumnae Director at my High School reached out to me via my blog and thought I would be a great speaker for the student body for Career Day. She wanted me to come and talk to the girls about how they too could find their Healthy Voice.

What's funny is that the date we scheduled for it came the two days after we buried my Dad and to when the date came across my email inbox I laughed out loud. I felt my Dad's spirit come through saying, "You are going to celebrate my life but then you are going to jump right in and pass this along to those Gwynedd girls!" He wasn't kidding.

It was an amazing experience to arrive in this place and see the change not just in the building but in my own spirit. I used to feel so inferior. The yearbook said I was most likely to become a Republican politician and now I was here being present to my truest self, my Healthy Voice. Mom came with me and I got to speak to a crowd of over 300 girls in uniform about my experience at Gwynedd and how I've come to know my Healthy Voice. I got to see old teachers and walk the hallways with my head held high. What I loved is that I got to meet a champion for the Healthy Voice that is in these girls' lives every day. Her name is Kate Tobias.

Kate has a "Think Tank" of girls. A few of them representing each class offered to do an interview with me for the book to discuss the different pressures of high school and how they cope with them. I am so grateful for their honesty and willingness to share! I think that their voices really represent what so many high-school students go through today. One freshman was trying to juggle time management between her school workload, being on the basketball team and trying to manage the responsibility of being the oldest of four at home. Another one said, "It's like you are trying to figure out who you are but then again trying to fit in with the rest of the school and beating yourself up." They cope with things like music, hanging out with family and taking breaks without thinking. The sophomore I spoke to talked about how different sophomore year is from freshman year. The whole goal is to get settled and adjusted but then stress starts about college. The juniors have intense time management stress with picking a college, filling out college applications, and bulking up your resume to get into your top choice. One girl copes by talking to her Mom and her friends, One senior said, "Senior year is so stressful. It is hardest year I have ever lived through." One girl feels pressure as the first in her family to go to college. Another senior felt pressure as the Captain of the field hockey team to be a role model for her peers. I asked them how they cope. One girl said she has a job on the side, "to get out of the house in order to not have a mental breakdown."

We talked about body image. The freshman talked about the increasing power of the media. One of the girls cited the influence of Victoria's Secret Fashion Show telling you to have a good, sexy body. This is when the girls started to talk more about what to eat, and how weight is something we can control. Another girl, a junior, said her Mom had always put an emphasis on her weight ever since she was a baby. A "good weight" is something she always wanted to achieve. Another student, an athlete, spoke of how she's never had anyone tell her she needs to lose weight. She knows she is MORE than her weight (Great Healthy Voice ™ for others!). But I knew from my own experience and what I see everyday that this kind of voice is so rare at this age!

Socially, these students feel pressure to be a good standing member of their class. One senior said, "If someone makes a bad decision, everyone in school knows and it hurts the reputation of the whole class." I asked about competition and perfectionism and one girl said something so beautifully honest. "I am my own worst enemy. I make myself feel bad about it to the point where I want to change it. So, I think, 'if someone does it better than me, I can do that too'." (Way to turn it into a Healthy Voice ™!) We did not even get to what some of these girls deal with in their Unhealthy Voice on a deeper level. I wanted to spend a whole week with them!

The Potential for Eating Disorders

I was reminded through these interviews and going back to my high school that there are many girls like me out there. To many people, we look like we've got it all together. We're Type-A. We're doing a million things. Yet, many times we're the ones who struggle the most with balance. That's where the vulnerability to the Unhealthy Voice and eating disorders becomes prevalent because they are looking for something to control when everything seems out of control. Just like the obesity issue, the divorce issue, and any other issue beneath the surface—this illustrates why it is so important not to just look for the signs of eating disorders on the surface. At a time like this, when these kids are so vulnerable—telling them they need to lose weight or eat something or that they are "fine" because they are eating healthy or working out, could be disguising a deeper problem.

I found this description on the American Academy of Child and Adolescent Psychiatry website and I think it really speaks to this concept.

A teenager with anorexia nervosa is typically a perfectionist and a high achiever in school. At the same time, she suffers from low self-esteem, irrationally believing she is fat regardless of how thin she becomes. Desperately needing a feeling of mastery over her life, the teenager with anorexia nervosa experiences a sense of control only when she says "no" to the normal food demands of her body. In a relentless pursuit to be thin, the girl starves herself. This often reaches the point of serious damage to the body, and in a small number of cases may lead to death.[4]

That afternoon at my former high school, I spoke honestly about my behaviors and the progression of my addiction in college and beyond. I wanted them to be aware of what could happen if they make unhealthy choices and to know it's not just about the moment but can have longer, deeper consequences. I wanted them to see that, I may have it all together from the outside, but it took a hard road and it still takes work every day to stay on the right road. I wanted to be an example for that one girl who may head down that road and not know where to turn. I wanted them to know getting to college wasn't just about hanging out with the right crowd and not picking up the drink but recognizing how you maybe react to things emotionally and physically. If they could see from my experience where they don't want to go, maybe someday they will remember "that girl Meredith" and get some hope for a new day.

The Presence of God at This Time in my Life

When I went back to Gwynedd I spoke quite a bit about how much my relationship with God has become a huge source of strength in my life, where it was conflicted before. I look back and find it so amazing how much my eyes were focused in the opposite direction of the light. I was focused on the dark. "I have to lose this weight. I have to get that guy. I have to be popular. I have to get into Notre Dame." These were all the things I thought I needed to be good enough. All the while, God was in the other direction and I couldn't see him. He was over the horizon calling me. It was as if he'd written me a letter. He came shining through as my Healthy Voice and I wanted to share with you the reader what he said. It's like a letter to my younger self, and to yours.

Dear Beloved,

First of all, you are good enough for me! You always have been and always will be.

You will think that many things outside of you—like looks, boys and grades will bring you value.

But your greatest value is right inside of you.

It's my love for you and I gave it to you before you were born.

Nothing you can do will ever take that away. It's constant.

So whatever happens on the road of life, know that your worth is not something you have to achieve.

You've already got it. Everything else is just a beautiful manifestation of who you are becoming in this life.

Know that you will be temped to find the answers to your deepest needs in those things outside of you, but your deepest needs can only be felt in that space created within you.

It's a space I created just for the relationship between you and I. It's a special one. So protect it with all your heart.

Know that no matter what your weight, your grades, how you or someone else portrays you right now—the love I have for you is what matters. Don't listen to that Unhealthy Voice.

Don't let it tell you that the scale determines your weight.

Reach for your dreams but go easy on yourself as you work towards them. I've got a plan that's awesome and I just need you to meet me halfway. So there is no need to try and be perfect.

Be grateful for the presence of your parents in your life today because someday they won't be there.

Be inspired by friends who will stand by you, music and role models who do the same.

Always stay true to yourself. Take the time to get to know your self and love yourself.

The light you create will shine forth everywhere you go.

Know that you are just getting your stride and life just gets better if you roll with everything it brings. Remember that you've got a whole life ahead of you. It's not a race. It's a journey. There's a lot of living and learning you have yet to do. So just enjoy the ride.

Oh and one more thing, we all have fears and insecurities. So when that Unhealthy Voice is trying to get you down like it will even when you are a grownup, just remember that I gave you a Healthy Voice.

I will always have your back and I love you more than you can ever know.

—Love, God (Your greatest Healthy Voice)

Every young adult deserves to know their worth goes beyond anything they are trying to achieve on the journey whether it's academics, sports or whatever! Of course we want to work at being the best in the class and build up our resumes for college, but we also get to be real and deserve to find the Healthy Voice within us. So I brought to my high school, to this book, and to any high schools I visit in the future—the hope of the

Healthy Voice. I choose to call out the Unhealthy Voice that kept me so blinded at such a beautiful time in my life so that I could call out for anyone at that age that might be clouded as well, the gift of the Healthy Voice!

One of the constant themes of my speech was about how I did not know God was there then, but I know he is now and I trust Him. He is why I do not need to control, or even fear what is around the corner. Yet, it certainly doesn't mean I don't try to! But I can always trust He has everything under control. He's got that light, that seed inside of us planted to give us all the beauty and energy we need to shine. That day, I shared a scripture passage, which has been a huge part of my journey and continues to be.

> *"Trust in the Lord with all your heart and lean not on your own understanding. In all your ways submit to Him and he will make your paths straight."*
> —*NIV, Proverbs 3:5*

One of the things I heard after my speech in some breakout sessions troubled me. It was how unaware some of the young women were of how present God is in their lives. "He's up there, not down here." "It's hard to find a relationship with Him because it's so forced upon us," and "Going to Catholic school, you are just saying the prayer by habit." One girl even said to me, "Faith is just a gift, and I've not had the pleasure of receiving it." Another said she was never forced into religion so she just chose to be agnostic. I believe each of us truly has to find our own walk with God, but each one of us as I saw in these girls that day deserves to find that he's in our hearts, minds, and spirits at every moment that we breathe. He's not limited to textbooks, sermons and church on Sundays. He is so much bigger than that! I wanted so much more for them in that moment! Instead I listened. I could relate so deeply to that experience and I prayed in that moment that someday I'd be able to be present for young women like them feeling the power of God in their lives when they were ready for a relationship.

I have to say, that day I was there with my Mom and it's funny because it made it really special regarding all of this God stuff because I've always credited her with being the one who laid the foundation for my faith. Her undying love and reliance on God during hard times showed me that I could do the same. Even though it would take me a lot longer to really understand that, I'd see how relying on Him would be the most grounding thing in my life, no matter what happened. Although we have taken different walks with our faith, I truly believe we are connected deeply on that spiritual level because of that seed she planted for a deep love of God in my heart. It's because she had me turn to Him, even if I didn't want to go to church, even if I was angry with Him that I stand so firmly on Him today. I'm forever grateful to my Mom for the tremendous seed of faith she planted that has blossomed and continues to blossom into such beauty as it does today.

Speaking of the inspiring music that I think speaks to so many young women of this age, I wanted to mention that I posted a blog for those girls at Gwynedd with a song from a band, Tenth Avenue North called "You Are More".

You can go to YouTube and watch the video to get the real message of love. It's amazing what the power of music and video can do to make you realize the power of God's love.

CHAPTER THREE:

Navigating College with an Unhealthy Voice

Starting college is much like starting high school. You want to fit in and be accepted more than ever because you don't have the safety net of your friends and family around to catch you when you fall. It's an exciting and scary time all at once. You show up on campus with both an Unhealthy and a Healthy Voice, like the world is at your fingertips but it's just so big! I showed up on Notre Dame's campus with that heavy Unhealthy Voice that was still trying to hold me back. I barely even noticed it at the time, but it was focusing on how I was different. Before I even met someone, I was sizing up how my SAT scores, my looks, and my weight weren't nearly enough. I was thinking about how different I was because I was the transfer student who was going to have to work harder at school and at making friends because I was a year behind. I was even thinking about how every person must have the perfect Catholic family and I was the only one with divorced parents. It's amazing how caught up in my head I was. On top of that, I was thinking about the people I missed back home—my two best friends from Gettysburg College where I'd went freshman year that I left and my Mom. Boy did I feel guilty and awful. Literally that voice was like a stick beating me in my mind over and over again.

Thankfully, my Dad drowned it out. He was my Healthy Voice at the time. He knew I was good enough for Notre Dame and that was enough for me. His excitement for this new journey and his positive attitude energized me. He was such a light in my life. I can still see his beaming smile right now and how he hit me on the arm like he always did when he was excited. "Isn't this great Meredith? You are going to love it here!" he said. He kept the light shining by coming out for football games and weekends every year and that was what carried me through it all. He always said that God and Grandmom were watching over me while I was there. Once Dad left campus though, the Unhealthy Voice remained. In fact, it got louder because it felt like I'd been left in the ocean without a lifeboat. I couldn't catch a break from that voice and it took everything I had to get ahead of it. See, I thought I was strong because I grew up the only child in a divorced family, but I'd also been very well taken care of all my life. I'd been shown the way. This was the first time I was going to have to do it on my own. It's just that this time it was a really hard school and I was very far from home with a very loud Unhealthy Voice. That Unhealthy Voice didn't care because all it knew was that this was just another new environment to load the gun and pull the trigger.

My Relationship with Alcohol and Food

This is the point in my story where I can look back and see how my disease of addiction progressed into a whole new realm all because one thing came into play—alcohol. It's a substance that every college kid confronts and often abuses. For many, it's one that can have consequences that infiltrate many facets of their life, like it did mine. Knowing what I know today about how alcohol affected my weight, my relationships, my academics, my insecurities, and my confidence—I can say it is a substance I never want to have to pick up again. With God in my life,

I will continue one day a time to surrender it because I never want to have to go to the places it took me. I share honestly about my relationship with it here, and how it progressively got worse because I know too many young adults who have suffered dramatically from it's affects. It doesn't mean they won't drink, but maybe just one young adult will read this and make a different choice when the time is right. The truth is, it doesn't matter how old you are, knowing my relationship with food, I know it's the same thing as my relationship with alcohol. There are way too many Americans who struggle with the two together and I hope this section gives those who might recognize the connection within themselves, some hope.

When I finally picked up my first drink it was like a breath of fresh air, not in a good way. It made me forget about my fears and inhibitions, and it suppressed my Unhealthy Voice. I felt like I had finally arrived. I'd found the thing that made me fit in with everyone else and I didn't have to worry about how I looked, my social status, or how good my grades were because I could drink well. Yet, I was a disaster on the inside. Even though I didn't love the taste, I wanted more of that escape. I craved it. I wanted to not think. I also loved the "permission" it gave me to overeat. The physical cravings the alcohol in my system gave me for food like burgers, sugar, baked goods and salty things were intense. I could barely focus on schoolwork because my body wasn't present. School didn't come easily to me anyway, but with the physical cravings on top of it, I was very challenged. I was amazed at how easily schoolwork came to so many of my friends. It was yet another reason for my Unhealthy Voice to beat me up.

My addictions, which none of us could see on the outside, were growing stronger on the inside. The disease I still hadn't identified loved the binge drinking culture of college. It especially loved tailgating season every fall. My friends and I prided ourselves on the tailgates we hosted. Our spot was prime real estate for the best tailgates in all of the parking lots. We would start our mornings off with a popped can of beer and a

Burger King breakfast sandwich. We would pick up our subs, cases of beer and head to the parking lot for a very long day of partying which did not have to end at kickoff. We would go and buy more cases for the car during the game to keep the party going. It was like a sport unto itself—from the beer can shotgun contests to the cups tournaments and post game parties. It was like the night never ended. I loved this time of the year, but I would also absolutely fear the uncontrollable. I knew deep down how intense my cravings would get when I hit those parking lots on game day with the amount of alcohol present and all the food around to eat. I feared that loss of control every football weekend. Not only that, as the season went on, I feared the progressive weight gain. I'd watch my friends and wonder why they weren't packing on weight like I was so fast. I had spent a lifetime trying to maintain my weight and here I was completely sabotaging it. I felt awful about myself and could not for the life of me figure out why I was packing on exponentially more weight when we were all drinking and eating the same thing. All I could think about was the last diet I went on at the end of the first semester freshman year. I came home for Christmas and gained so much weight that Dad had me go on a diet of powder and fro-yo. I didn't want to have to do the dining hall for another semester like that. So embarrassing.

I found out just how out of control the alcohol was going to get early on that sophomore year. It was soon after trying out for the women's crew team when two of my roommates had to rescue me from St. Joe Hospital in the wee hours of the morning. I had gone to the crew team initiation party and exhibited my drinking abilities with the guy's team. I took liters worth of their concoction, "Yucca," a combination of vodka, lemons and limes, and straight sugar. This led to a hospital visit within 24 hours and a doctor telling me, "You have a serious alcohol problem. You can't drink." I was terrified as I knew the gene was in my family, but because I was in college where you "have" to drink, I had to keep it a secret because I was afraid I wouldn't be accepted if I told people I couldn't drink.

I remember when my friend Meghan dropped me off at Main Circle and handed the plastic bag full of my clothes from that night. I looked at her and said, "Oh my Gosh, how nice! They dry cleaned my clothes for me!" At the time we thought it was hysterical and it continued to be a story for ages to come in my drinking career but it really wasn't funny. It was that moment when my body told me drinking wasn't something I could do in moderation. It was that moment the gene showed it's face but because of my fear combined with a lack of understanding of kids who just have the gene and can't drink—I went deeper into it. That was a defining moment in my life and it continues to be one of the reasons I fight for those kids who do have moments like that when they go out at night. People think it's willpower but in many cases, they showed up on that campus with a gene they aren't conscious of, an Unhealthy Voice and an environment that triggers the disease. It's got nothing to do with the calories or the moderation of the drink. It is what it is, and it's those kids who need a different kind of compassion and attention.

Many just continue on the road of destruction. If they are anything like me, keeping it a secret and trying to pretend they can handle their drinking brings up a lot of shame and a lot of, "Why can't I just handle this?" If they have the weight factor, it only quadruples the shame. What's worse is that when you cope with the food or alcohol to deal with feelings, you are stuck in this crazy cycle. You can't get out on the inside and on the outside you can barely look at yourself because you feel like you look like a balloon. You hate yourself because you can't resist all the snacks your roommates are grazing on around the dorm rooms or picking up at the student center late night. You don't even want to eat at the dining hall, let alone pizza late at night because you feel like any food will just make you blow up more but you have to eat. You see the food and you want it too. It's a nightmare where you have no control over your body or cravings. The Unhealthy Voice takes over.

That hospital incident wasn't my only one. Because my drinking continued, my consequences did as well. I broke my ankle at tailgates twice. I broke my nose in my 5th year (you'd think I would have learned by then) by physically running into a friend that I was running towards to hug. Not only that, I felt awful about how my parents were seeing me. Dad didn't like coming to our tailgates and I'd fear the look from him when I'd come into the stadium to sit with him because I knew he knew. Then, the one time Mom came to visit for a game I hurt her because of my actions with the drinking. It just wreaked havoc and I hated myself for not being able to control it with willpower.

The intensity of the Unhealthy Voice was overwhelming. I couldn't believe how much worse it had gotten since I got there. It's not like I wasn't having fun, it's just that I was dying on the inside. I was afraid, stressed, feeling broken, flawed, and ashamed. I had absolutely no sense of love for myself and definitely no Healthy Voice. I couldn't feel the spirit within me. The alcohol and the food were the addictions running and ruining my life. I was crying out for an escape from the craziness. I wanted to get grounded and at the time I had no sense of it. All of my friends were picking programs to go abroad and I got the idea to choose the land of my ancestors. That had to get me rooted, right? I was so excited because I was going back to the roots of my Dad's Mom and my Mom's Dad in Ireland. But I was also going back to the roots of my powerful alcoholic disease where genetics would load the gun yet again and environment would pull the trigger.

Going Abroad to Cork, Ireland

I showed up for my study abroad experience in Ireland with my Unhealthy Voice more intact than ever. I was definitely looking for what we call in recovery, a "geographical cure." I wanted this place to fix me and take me away from all of my troubles back home. I wanted to be there because I knew I'd find people who spoke English that were genuine and real. That's what I wanted. I also knew the land was beautiful and lush and I wanted to experience as much as I could. But my disease had a different plan.

Most days we went to school at University College Cork. We'd have lunch, which typically consisted of bread and potatoes, and maybe a pint. Then we'd walk home and stop for pints so we could go out later and have more pints, then end up at the pub attached to our apartment complex. I couldn't escape it, and what's worse—this beer was heavy. So I was packing on the weight like nobody's business. I felt completely disconnected from myself physically, mentally, emotionally, and spiritually. So I grabbed on for dear life to something. That something was the alcohol. It was also the emergency credit card of my parents that I used to shop and call friends back at home. I was irresponsible and I hated myself for being irresponsible. It was just another thing to add to the shame list, for that stupid Unhealthy Voice. The only thing that kept me vibrant and alive were the great friends I met, the month backpacking around Europe and all the beautiful scenery in Ireland I got to experience. Otherwise, that time was one of the hardest in my life. I had reached my heaviest weight and it felt like I was almost in a vacuum. I was so far from home that I feared what my family would think of me when they saw me. I'd lost myself to this place. I tried to eat healthy and do some running but it wasn't working.

When it was time to leave Ireland, I hated myself and above all, my body. I was utterly terrified of going back to the United States and getting back into the real world. I would have to deal with real life. I had spent too much money. I drank too much. I ate too much. It was all too much. Now, I would have to go face the people who knew me best. There would be no more hiding.

My defense was to blame my parents. They planted the disease when they got divorced and caused these behaviors. I had no idea. We had no idea that this gene was in my body and they weren't to blame. My plan was to demand they fix the mess. I knew how I looked. I knew it was going to be a shock. I was hurting so badly and I did not know what else to do. So, I got off that plane. Immediately, I saw in my Dad's eyes his concern about my weight. I just said, "Don't worry Dad. I know I look like a pint of Guinness; but the weight is coming off." It was going to be all about the weight, this alcohol problem. I will never forget yelling at my parents in Mom's living room. I took my anger out on them. Out of nowhere I said, "Dad! I am sick of working for free. I have to learn how to make money because I just spent a load of money that wasn't mine and I'm never going to grow up if I keep doing that!" Then I said, "This divorce screwed me up. I'm done. I'm ready to deal with it or I'm going to suffocate from the pain it's caused me!"

Like that moment I was in the hospital sophomore year, this time coming home from Ireland is when I realized that alcohol was a real problem for me. At the time, I couldn't pin it down because to me it was just something to control in my diet. The weight is what we all saw though. So, we did the one and only thing we thought to do, treat the weight. We found Dr. Pamela Peeke, M.D. whom I mentioned earlier. This woman would teach me how to eat for life, not diet. She taught me to fuel my body with food and made me think 'healthy lifestyle.' She even told me I'd be a marathon runner someday. I did not believe it at the time, but she was right. Dr. Peeke played a pivotal role in my life. She was the first Healthy Voice in my life to help me find grounding in my body. Dr. Peeke also had me weight training to help speed up my metabolism. I also started running to get the weight off. Most importantly, Dr. Peeke made me believe I was an athlete. That gave me tremendous confidence for the long haul. I have healthier habits today due to the seeds she planted! Years later, little did we know, our lives would intersect again professionally.

Finding God's Presence at Notre Dame

All that time I was suffering in my disease I didn't know God was present within me or beside me. I could only see Him like I'd seen him since I was a kid. He was in my religion class over in DeBartolo Hall or in the Basilica at Sunday mass, at the grotto or in the dorm mass on

Sunday night, but he wasn't with me. He was always separate. I was always thinking I had to somehow get good enough for him. That little girl inside of me that feared he didn't love me because of my weight or my parents divorce still came with me when I'd go to mass. I felt unloved and different from everyone else. What I didn't know yet was that I'd just come to know him in a different way and at the time I needed to know he was with me, even though I didn't feel it. I was just going through the motions, which sometimes we have to do. I'd go to church with Dad and Diane on Sunday morning for the smells and bells mass. I'd go to the grotto to light a candle. I'd go through the motions of my faith, never feeling worthy of His love. But I was . . .

It's funny because now, it's amazing how much I feel the presence of God, of His Holy Spirit and of Dad's spirit really when I am on Notre Dame's campus. It is so powerful that it brings me to tears almost regularly. I feel so much love and peace I can't even believe it. It makes me realize why I almost had to be in that deep struggle and feeling of separation from God when I was here as an undergraduate student so that I could feel the overwhelming power of God's grace and love today. It's truly become a spiritual place for me. My family and I used to laugh about how Dad wanted every kid in the extended family to go to Notre Dame and I'd say how I was the "sacrificial lamb" that had to go. Now I can say that I am truly the lucky one that got to go and get to have this experience on a regular basis where I can connect to God, to nature, and even to Dad. It's the place that has held me in my struggles and healed me in my recovery. The memories I have here are countless and I am grateful. From darkness I have come into light.

"If you could find a way to bottle the Notre Dame Spirit, you could light up the universe."

—Joe Theisman

The Need for A Healthy Voice Presence on College Campuses

College campuses are a breeding ground for the Unhealthy Voice to pounce on any student's weaknesses. It's got nothing to do with how they perform academically or how they appear to be on the outside and everything to do with how they are on the inside. It's why I believe so many college students are in need of a Healthy Voice to help them navigate college and get them ready for life after. Many kids are struggling with insecurities that they think they have to cover up in order to measure up. So they do what everyone does. They workout, work hard in school, try to eat right, find a good guy, get good grades, and have fun on the weekends. They maintain composure pretty well, until something happens with the Unhealthy Voice. Something doesn't go their way. Weight is gained. Alcohol incident interferes. Guy stuff happens. Grades get bad or something happens back home and everything gets a little hairy. Yet, they just keep pushing through because it's all about looking like you've got everything under control even though you are falling apart beneath the surface, freaking out about your weight or what happened that night you drank too much. On top of that, you add in what might be knowledge of a punishing God, and these kids are sending themselves into a virtual self-shame storm. It's a deadly combination for an Unhealthy Voice to bubble up into isolation that leads to things like depression, eating disorders, or alcohol abuse.

That illusion of control is a complete façade of the Unhealthy Voice. It makes a young, promising college student that's got the world at her fingertips believe that everything rests on one thing. That one thing could be grades, the boy, popularity, weight-loss, or an athletic goal but if they don't reach that goal, everything will fall apart. That's where the Unhealthy Voice comes in and makes you believe that your worth is not already within you but outside of you. It's when any one of us can forget that our self-worth is within us and go head first in the opposite direction thinking it's outside of us. Then when we don't get exactly what we want when we want it, we feel absolutely and utterly defeated and I think college is when this shows up in full force because everyone thinks they are alone, but they are not.

Every woman in college has a Healthy Voice within them and deserves to hear it. It's not based on anything outside of them, but the worth they carry within them. It's not about looking like you've got it all together, but working to be your best and knowing that you can be yourself no matter what because you've got people walking the journey with you who love you for who you are. The whole isolating shame that so many girls have around food, boys, looks, and drinking in college, is one big fat Unhealthy Voice that lies. College is a time when kids are away from home. They seek a place that feels like home and often times the only place like that is their dorm room. But sometimes the dorm room isn't safe either because there is food lying around or distractions that bring out the Unhealthy Voice. That's why my goal is to help provide girls with the knowledge and power within them to shine their Healthy Voice so that no matter where they are on campus they know they are okay. I'm all about planting this seed of the Healthy Voice Perspective in as many young college women as I can. I believe it will bring a human connection to carry them through college and beyond that is so much deeper than just a simple friendship.

Drinking: The Great Saboteur

I've shared what drinking did to me and how it plays out some on college campuses. Yet, I believe it's important to call it out like the issue of weight, divorce, and eating disorders. You can't ignore it but you also can't keep shouting out statistics to change it. You've got to get to the root of it. So here are some staggering statistics as well as what I believe what we are doing and how we can change that to do something different about the problem for college kids and beyond.

The general statistics of how college students are abusing alcohol are staggering. According to the Centers for Disease Control (CDC), about

90% of the alcohol consumed by youth under the age of twenty-one in the US is in the form of binge drinking. The highest proportion was in the 18-20 year-old group, citing 51% who binge. The CDC also estimates that binge drinkers account for more than half of the 79,000 annual deaths related to alcohol that occur in the U.S. with about six percent of them (4,675) being under the age of twenty-one.[5] "Drunkorexia" has become rampant on college campuses where the alcohol is a food and calorie replacement. A study by the University of Missouri of 1,000 students found that a substantial segment (almost 16%) of the student population was choosing not to buy groceries or eat meals but instead binge on alcohol in order to save money and slim down. According to a website called collegebingedrinking.net, a study at the University of North Carolina, found that women with disordered eating were actually more comfortable admitting to their abuse of alcohol then they were confessing to anorexia or bulimia, yet those who suffer from combined disordered eating and binge drinking were at greater risk for sexual encounters, violence, substance abuse, and alcohol poisoning.[6] Then students go abroad and "drink twice as much as they did before going abroad."[7] These are just some of the statistics.

What is clear is that kids are turning to alcohol, like I did and so many others do, to cope with stress and to have fun. Many believe it is harmless, but many have the potential genetic predisposition inside of them that could be lethal and they walk onto a college campus not even knowing about it. All they get is a class or a warning from their parents about what too much alcohol can do or the gene in their family, but until they have that experience, they don't know. That is scary stuff because that's the stuff that gives one kid alcohol poisoning countless times or excessive weight gain and another kid no trouble. Kids deserve to know before they pick up things like why they might want to drink, what they know about the genes in their family and what their relationship with alcohol has been in the past. They don't deserve to go into it blindly. Does it mean they won't choose to drink? No. But giving them a choice in the matter rather than a lecture could make all the difference.

Remember, it's not about how much they drink or how many calories it is or whatever. It's about what they are going to it for and what it does for them. They deserve to know there are healthy alternatives that won't be so destructive in their lives, especially for those kids who do end up in the hospital and are ashamed. They can make a different choice and listen to their Healthy Voice. They need to know that alcoholism isn't just old men who drink every day or bums that live under a bridge. It's being out of control with alcohol and using it as an escape. They need to get familiar with it and be aware of what it does to their mind, body, and spirit! Trying to get a kid who is out of control with alcohol to control it is next to impossible and often painful for them because it makes them feel ashamed that they can't control it. It's pretty awful. It can eat them alive and affect their studies and whole college experience. I've seen it happen all too often.

Sometimes, sadly, girls are even shamed by their own peers. One of my girls once told me that she came home in the middle of the night to her roommate. She had been sexually assaulted, with bruises to show for it, and went to her roommate in trust who said, "You always seem to get yourself in these situations. You're just one of those girls who just can't control herself, aren't you?" Her quote to me was, "I learned quickly to shut up and move on in silence, as so many girls learn at Notre Dame." It happens all the time on so many campuses, not just Notre Dame. It happens with alcohol too. I've been asked to speak at a dorm once where a handful of girls drank too much one night and all had consequences. I was grateful to go and talk about what alcohol did to me and share the truth about my relationship with it. It was amazing how many girls said, "I wish I'd heard this before!" Alcohol isn't about calories. It's not a weight-control thing. To me, you can either drink it or you can't. It's up to you to determine that. For me there wasn't any amount of dieting, working out, or trying to get good enough in anything that would make it's power over me go away until I stopped using it.

Dieting: The Weight is the Big Control Illusion

It's amazing to me how intense the culture of body image is prevalent on college campuses. It doesn't shock me but sometimes it overwhelms me when I hear from my girls how bad it really gets. The competition is fierce to look good, dress well, be popular, eat healthy, and workout. You would think academics were competitive enough, but this area feeds right into the cultural obsession with body image so it makes sense. It breeds the dieting and bingeing for many college girls and an obsession with weight-control. Then you add in the drinking and it's one big ugly mess that you feel like you just can't control and have to compete. Their fears are masked by this intense competition around body and weight, often times trying to tell each other what to do and it creates a massive Unhealthy Voice that I'm all about changing.

Since weight is a barometer for a lot of young college women like the ones I've coached, I know the Unhealthy Voice starts as soon as they get on the scale in the morning. It literally determines their self-worth for the day. Eating means restricting calories and whatever your current personal "food rules" are. Food triggers are everywhere. The dining hall is an overwhelming place for buffets of not knowing what to eat, friends watching what you eat, telling you how and what to eat, and cravings calling your name. The dorms aren't any better. Junk food is everywhere even if you try not to have it in your room. Parents send care packages of baked goods across the hall and try as you might you can't resist them. Then you hate yourself when you give into the visual craving. Vending machines are down the hall. Student center with all if it's snacks is walking distance away and the weekend is coming soon for more drinking and late night overeating, which you know will only make you feel worse about your weight. Being with these girls as they navigate this stuff, I could feel in my bones how hard it was to be in that space when food has such a powerful space and you are trying to "measure up" with the body competition. Then girls get in their heads and wonder why they can't just chomp on snacks lying around the dorm room like everyone else and not get in their heads or gain a pound. Girls are going to the gym and getting on the treadmill, sometimes so long that they pass out from not eating. There are no regulations to stop them from going any further. Others are knee deep in eating disorders and too afraid to go to the counseling center and appear weak. They feel like they've got to keep dieting so they can compete with the rest of them. It is an insane battlefield of girls fighting the front lines of the Unhealthy Voice and it's ugly!

When I was writing this I had the opportunity to speak with an old friend from college who was almost a mirror to me in the sense of the Unhealthy Voice prevalent in our college life. When we were in college together, we did not realize we were both struggling with such an intense Unhealthy Voice going through some of the same issues. We both were trying to control our weight and struggling with "landmines in college." We spoke about how envious we were of people who ate "normally" or how fascinated we were by one of our roommates who could stop eating when she was full. She would leave part of her sandwich in her wrapper and we would both be thinking, *"Are you going to eat that? If not, I will!"* We talked about how drinking gave us an excuse to eat and how we were both magnets for problem eating from the minute we met. She said, "There was something about how we could relate to each other and I am convinced it had to do with food." She even said, "Can I be honest with you? I was happy when we were not living together our senior year because I knew our friendship was toxic." We were competitive about our "claim" to be healthy when we were actually dying from this Unhealthy Voice on the inside. She even told me a story about how I got angry with her for exercising and competing with me. I had made it about making myself feel bad for not being as fit as her. We had a constant competition with food and exercising. At the time, we really did not know our "healthy living" created something toxic between us and the funny part is over ten years later we realize how connected we are in spirit with our stories. If we'd only not been in such competition we may have been able to share our struggles.

I'm truly amazed by those young women who can stand in the face of it and not get down from it. I admire those girls who don't have a struggle with food and would be what you consider "normal" eaters because they don't get in their heads, hearts or bodies when they eat. It's not an emotional experience. To them, it is just food. I'm not one of those people and never will be. I have to set boundaries with it and I'm fine with that. It doesn't mean there is something wrong with me. It just means food is the area where I need to take care of myself a little bit more because it's where my Unhealthy Voice wants to bring me down first. I share this because I've seen too many girls make this their weakest link and compare themselves to those friends of theirs that do eat "normal" and wonder why they can't too. They wonder why they can't just have that body. Yet, nobody has the same body or the same food needs! If they can just let that go and operate with what they've got, they've got it made because you can't control what you can't control! Every girl has got to find her own Healthy Voice when it comes to food and fitness because everybody needs different fuel to operate. That's why getting it in college is so crucial because they don't have to carry a weight obsession into the real world! I'm all about promoting healthy lifestyles, but I'm more about promoting them for kids in a holistic way. If I meet a girl, I want her to be her absolute best self in a physical, mental, emotional, and spiritual way. We've got to shake off for these kids the idea that physical is everything, mental or emotional weakness is failure, and spirituality isn't as important as academics.

For me, that spiritual component was the missing piece and often times when I work with young women, that is exactly what they are looking for. They are looking to fill that deeper need that only the power that created them can fill. It's not something I can give them, but it's something I can share how I lost and found it again. It's something I can maybe guide them to through my own experience and tools but it's up to them to find that deeper relationship with God in their own hearts. My only hope is that they take it out of the books, the churches and whatever they've known and realize his lover is bigger than anything they could ever imagine. I am immensely grateful to the character and values that my education at Notre Dame planted for me. I also love the spirit of the tradition of Notre Dame, but for me, and any person who steps foot on this campus—we all have our own special spiritual connection with this place. We just have to find it.

The Blossoming of the Healthy Voice

I can't wait to see how the Healthy Voice blossoms on college campuses. I've already started to see it in the girls I've coached, the young women God puts in my path to meet and the college audiences I've spoken to already. I just know girls are going to take it and run. Why? Well, another funny thing happened right after my father passed. I was invited to speak back at my college dorm, Walsh Hall, on Notre Dame's campus with the local Girls on the Run chapter. How weird it was to be sharing the hope in the place where all the chaos began for me. Yet, God had me right where he wanted me! I shared my story and at the end there weren't enough cards to go around. I had to write my email and website down on Subway napkins. Girls thanked me, asked me when my book was coming out, told me they wished they'd met me freshman year and told me I spoke right to their hearts. My old dorm is a short walk from the grotto and so after I spoke I walked down there to thank God for the experience and Dad for being my light. I was so grateful to be present to them as a channel for God and this Healthy Voice. I can only imagine what more God has planned for me with girls just like these. Wings to fly, permission to be themselves and accepted in the world is what these girls want.

One particular girl came up to me that night whose name was Sarah and she was this bright, beautiful light that actually reminded me of myself. By appearance she had all the confidence in the world and was gorgeous. She shared with courage about how much she related to my story and how committed she was to turning down her Unhealthy Voice and how she wanted me to show her the way to her Healthy Voice. The work we did together and the light she's become for the Healthy Voice that shines out has been beautiful to watch, because I know her for who she is on the inside and that's what we all want. It's funny because towards the end of the school year, she and I were in a yoga class together and I got to see how much she'd grown. I got to witness her Healthy Voice in full effect. It was a full class for my friend Roxie that teaches a fabulous Hot Yoga class filled with a lot of college students. For any kid filled with the voice of competition it could be ripe for the Unhealthy Voice. I walked into the room, laid my mat next to Sarah and leaned in. She smiled at me and I knew what she was thinking. Shining your Healthy Voice and being yourself in a world that is all about being perfect on the outside isn't easy! Because she was tuned in, I was too. All I had to do was lean in and say, "Hey you, stay on your mat." What a moment, and the amazing part is that being present to her made me think about the other girls in the class who were searching around the room comparing themselves. This Healthy Voice thought came to my mind that seemed so appropriate I saved it for this:

We are so much stronger together in our weaknesses. Through competition, we think we will be the strongest if we get to the top. Through our shared weaknesses, we can lift each other up as we travel on the journey, or in that case, on the mat.

So many young women make it about competition and control, even in the yoga studio. We have to ease up on ourselves! We get to find our own personal Healthy Voice together and we don't have to worry about what everyone else is doing! The greatest adventure you will ever take in life is the one within. Although it may be hard at times, it's worth it because it will endure.

My Healthy Voice Girls

One of the best things about beginning the journey is that you get to be part of the tribe of the Healthy Voice. The girls that God has brought into my life have been a huge blessing and I am so grateful to have been part of their journey. I am also honored to keep witnessing their growth on the path. They all are walking their own journey taking their own steps forward, navigating their own setbacks, and doing it all with reliance on a Higher Power, a consciousness of the Healthy Voice within them and a knowledge that it's all going to work out in the end. They know that the Unhealthy Voice loves to get them comparing, competing, trying to be perfect or thinking they aren't good enough. They also know it tries to make them think their self-worth is based on a boy or a career/academic accomplishment, but they always get back to their truth. They know it's not about being perfect or getting their self-worth outside of themselves. It's about being perfectly imperfect, navigating through the journey and enjoying every step. For one girl it will try to defeat her with an athletic injury. For another it's the pant size at a store and for another it's still that weight voice. They are all on their own journey and getting over the bumps in the road as they come. I'm happy to have walked alongside them and can't wait to see where their Healthy Voice takes them in their careers, relationship, and in life. I just love that they are learning to be gentle on themselves and know that they can always rely on their Healthy Voice, even when the Unhealthy Voice wants to beat them up.

My hope is that all of these girls will connect in their stories and be stronger together so that that Unhealthy Voice of competition and fear that permeates through so many young women can be shattered and more of us can know we're all in this together. I just envision girls running races for their Healthy Voice, not because they want to beat up on their bodies.

I see girls having dinner to talk about how they are navigating life with it, not about gossip. I see it being a whole culture of Healthy Voice conversation and communication that opens up a unique positive atmosphere for any woman that wants to choose a positive outlook beyond the surface!

CHAPTER FOUR:

Being a Recent College Grad with an Unhealthy Voice

My Early 20s

Once I graduated from college, I was heading into the next phase of my life with no parachute and no roadmap, just a diploma and a gene that I didn't know about that was primed and ready to pull the trigger. This time the environment was Austin, Texas where I'd be working on a presidential campaign for Governor George W. Bush. If you've ever been in politics or worked on a campaign, you know the stress of the environment and the coping mechanisms people use to relieve stress. It can be a rather unhealthy space, especially for someone showing up with an intense Unhealthy Voice and not much armor to fight it.

Thanks to Dad's connections in the political world, I had an internship lined. At the time I had mixed feelings. The Unhealthy Voice part of me resented this because it felt like I wasn't getting this job on my own. I also wasn't even sure I liked politics, but the Healthy Voice part of me was surprisingly excited. I had met the Governor at an event a few months earlier. I was blown away. Having grown up around politicians, it felt like there was something different about him. I could tell he was real just by his handshake. That day I said to my Dad, "I've got to work for that guy." So when Dad told me I was going to be an intern for the chief strategist on the campaign, Karl Rove, I was up for it. Presidential politics had been part of my life for so many years with Dad and Diane's work that it seemed almost second nature, but this time the game was bigger. The pressure was higher and I was far away from home.

The Presidential Campaign in Austin, Texas

I had much of the same insecurities when I arrived in Austin as I did when I arrived at Notre Dame. "Am I going to be good enough?" was my nagging question. Everybody knew and loved my Dad at the campaign. That made the pressure more intense and the expectations that I put on myself higher. I somehow had to prove myself here. I put myself down for being the daughter of a high profile campaign advisor instead of realizing how lucky I was to get my foot in the door and have a job! I was more worried about what people thought of me than what I was learning. I felt very out of place coming from the east coast and South Bend, Indiana to this place they called Texas. I felt like a fish out of water. Thank God for that strong Healthy Voice in my father. He led me there and guided me as much as he could as I walked the path. I'll never forget that first day of work pulling up to 301 Congress Avenue. He was like a kid in a candy story dropping me off. I was so excited that he was so excited. I am so grateful my Dad could be a part of it. He lifted me up and got me started even though I was leaning heavily on his wings and not my own. It was a special time. Thankfully, his work frequently required him to make return visits to Austin which gave me regular bursts of energy much like when he'd come to South Bend for games. It made for great memories of those times together!

Of course the minute he would leave, the light would go out in some way. The Unhealthy Voice would bark and I'd feel powerless over it. It didn't matter how cool this opportunity was. It was still there and I hated it. That didn't matter because it loved this new environment. It is hard to truly describe what the inside of a presidential campaign looks like. It is a marathon going a hundred miles a minute. You are always running towards the finish line while deflecting attacks from the opposing team. There is no rest for the weary. It was one big game of whack-a-mole with my Unhealthy Voice shooting at me from every direction. The stress of the job was intense and I was lowest on the totem pole! I have no clue how people like the Governor and Karl handled it. I was working for Israel Hernandez "Izzy," Governor Bush's former aide and Karl's go-to man on a million things including direct mail. I was learning a lot about spreadsheets, staying up late tagging Israel with looking for edits on direct mail pieces to go out. Sometimes I was answering Karl's phone when his assistant Kristin wasn't at her desk. We were a tiny but very busy operation of interns called the "Lincoln Lounge" and we got things done! Yet, I was still always in fear I wasn't good enough. Thank God for Israel's leadership and guiding light. I just remember when the "red phone" would ring in Karl's office; this phone was solely used for incoming calls from Governor Bush. I would completely freeze when the Governor would ask for Karl in his thick Texas accent. I was like a kid who had just seen a ghost. The worst was I was asked to drive Karl up to the Governor's Mansion for a meeting. Oh my—fear! I would be so terrified that this guy was going to ask me something about politics and that I would get fired. Of course, it was never anything like that. As if the environment didn't give me enough stress, my internal Unhealthy Voice was beating me up with the "should stick" for not getting my own job, not being completely financially independent from my parents, not being there for Mom, not being better or more perfect! The external stress and the internal Unhealthy Voice were just overwhelming me. I was exhausted and the environment was ripe for my Unhealthy Voice to get what its fix.

At the office, the little kitchen right by our Strategy cubicles was where the "Cookie Lady" would leave her freshly baked cookies every day. All I had to do was go in there and grab them. People were always going outside for smoke breaks which I could do at any moment, and didn't even really enjoy it but anything to get an escape! After work we frequented Mexican places like Maudie's, which was introduced to me on my very first day on the job. It was in this dilapidated strip mall, connected to a Laundromat and Goodwill on either side. I had found my choice of "crack" for my entire time in Austin—Queso Dip, guacamole, chips, a margarita and fajitas became a regular fix at the end of the day. The bars were our other place to go. We went pretty much every night to places like our favorite rooftop patio, Speakeasy. Many of them were just steps away from the office and had such an appeal with their outdoor space, live bands on a regular basis, and fun drinks. You'd dream about them in the middle of the day as your escape.

That's all fine and good, but it's not so good when you've got an Unhealthy Voice that knows how you'll react to it. I knew it wasn't going to be good for me physically, mentally, or emotionally but I had no idea how to keep it under control. All I knew was that I was stressed. I needed to cope. I needed to fit in, and drinking was how I knew to do both. The problem was that I started to look like I did in Ireland and pack on the weight like a ton of bricks. The drinking and Mexican food eating became so second nature to us, that I became totally disconnected from my body, but it was there! It tasted good and we were having fun, so I just kept doing it. It was my escape. It also gave me the courage to start chasing some boys, which wasn't always good when I'd had one too many. But none of that was enough to make the pain of my weight-gain go away. I had to do something to change it. So, in the city of all cities that loves running, I started to get serious about mine.

Thankfully Town Lake, now called Lady Bird Lake, was just a few blocks away from our headquarters in downtown Austin. I decided to make the commitment to myself that I was going to lose this weight. I was going to run a 10K. I was going to find a way to deal with the stress that wasn't just about eating Mexican food and drinking. My Healthy Voice I didn't know yet was telling me there was another way. So I started bringing my gym bag to work and running around the lake every day when I had the chance. This is when I can look back and say I am truly grateful that my Mom planted the seed of running. For a long time as a teenager she'd try to get me to go out and run a mile around the block and I'd hate it. It was in this moment that I realized she was planting a seed for this very moment of growth.

Within a few short months I was calling her saying, "Hey Mom! I'm ready to run a marathon with you! Let's do Marine Corps!" She used to talk about how crazy I was that I wanted to do one that fast. (Yes, we addicts don't do anything half-assed.) It brought us closer and it was awesome to talk with her about training. I have a great picture and wonderful memory of Mom and I finishing that marathon together with our arms in the air crossing the finish line. We have so many awesome memories around running that I am grateful for each one. For me that time with Mom on a run symbolized that we were on the road together and like her faith, she taught me through the long distance running that life is truly a marathon, not a sprint. For that, I'm thankful.

There was something spiritual about this running for me. It was a very Healthy Voice. At that point in my life, it was literally giving me wings to fly. It was giving me the confidence I needed that I wasn't finding in the office or in myself. It still is a huge part of what grounds me today on the road of life. It was the first thing that really helped me lose the weight. It made me start making healthier food choices. It made me believe I was that athlete Dr. Peeke saw in me back in college. It's like my body was calling out for a healthy behavior and I answered the call just by taking some action. What's even better is that I got to run five marathons and I continue to run today, but there was a big change that happened in the middle.

I had a pretty powerful Unhealthy Voice when I started running too. Because of the place I was in at the time, so desperate for something to make me okay and good enough—I made that running something more. I made it my self-worth barometer. Not only that, I made it the thing that would cover up the eating disorder I struggled with for so long. This supposed healthy habit would become an unhealthy habit. It had become an addictive fix for me that would keep me from feelings I needed to feel. Eventually when I'd hit treatment, I'd have to stop running literally and figuratively to face myself. Running marathons was fun, but I used them to prove that I was good enough, beating myself up with every mile I'd run when I never had to do that. I could have my emotions and have my running at the same time, but my running would never make those emotions go away. What sucked was when I'd have to tell my Mom, who I'd run so many miles with in my life that I wasn't going to be able to run marathons anymore. Her knees weren't the best anyway so it wasn't such a bad thing. Yet, it felt like I'd severed an emotional tie between us that would take time to heal, but it wasn't up to me. We've all got to find our own way on the path.

I share this because I see so many people pick up running like I did and instead of making it part of their healthy lifestyle—they make it their identity like I did. They give too much power to the Unhealthy Voice. If that's where you are, or if you ever see yourself getting there—believe me—it is not your only self-worth. It just adds to it. You are not only a physical being. You are a spiritual and emotional being. Your self-worth is already within you. If you go into it with that Healthy Voice and attitude, you'll have it for life. If you go into it with an Unhealthy Voice, it could sabotage you and I wouldn't want that for you! I want you to run with your Healthy Voice!

Despite all the chaos with my Unhealthy Voice barking at me, I'm truly grateful to have been a part of the Bush-Cheney campaign. The memories I made with the people I worked with are ones that I cherish the most. We share battle stories and war wounds. We have shared memories of watching SNL working late into the night, going to the RNC conventions in Philadelphia and New York and moments that just make you laugh out loud when you think about them. Each one of those moments and people I shared them with means the world to me. My friends from the Lincoln Lounge and the people I worked with are the ones who knew me in a way that is so close to my heart. They knew the team Dad and I were and they share the memories of our long dinners together when he'd come into to town and we'd pontificate about politics or where our lives would take us. None of us would have ever thought the night of the election when we were writing our predictions on cocktail napkins that things would end up as they did. We'd all go back to the office that night clicking the refresh button on our computers until the wee hours of the morning. Karl would say to me, "Go home to bed Mere. We'll get them in the morning." We didn't but eventually everything worked out exactly how it was supposed to be and we all got to make our way back to my hometown of Washington once the Recount was finally over. Every time I think of that time, it just reminds me that all things work out in the end.

The White House

Post campaign, I was excited to be one of the chosen few going to the White House. I was also bringing all of my friends from Texas with me back to my home. Since I had grown up in Washington, D.C., and I had been to the White House so many times, I felt like I was in my comfort zone. I will never forget how surreal it was to walk into the Old Executive Office Building where I'd first met my stepmom as a kid. Now, I was walking in to work myself! How crazy it was. I was joining the Office of Public Liaison, which was in charge of all the President's events and outreach to the public. We had no roadmap for this endeavor except for a lot of missing 'W' keys from our computer keyboards. All we knew was that we had to do these events, get the right people there, and coordinate it all for the President of the United States. Yeah. Logistics, planning and inviting was our game and we sometimes had to get these from approvals to launch within one week. Thank goodness for teamwork and our dedicated White House interns or there is no way we would have gotten it all done. We were on the go constantly. We were implementing this week's events, coordinating next week's events, and even planning smaller events without the President.

It was intense but it was also really fun to see the Presidential event you put together fall into place. It was exhilarating and also exhausting every time you finished one.

As for my Unhealthy Voice, it loved the intensity of this place they call the White House. It still wanted me to believe that I wasn't good enough, even though I was surrounded with people that were like family. Underneath it all I was trying to measure up on a whole new level. I wanted to make Dad and Diane happy through my work in this place and I didn't want to hurt Mom by choosing this job. It wasn't at all about what I needed and more about what they wanted for me. I was attached to this connection with my Dad around politics. My emotions went between the rush of the experience and beating myself up for following dad to D.C. I felt so ashamed to have chosen politics. I was never just myself. I was either riding the high of being on top of the world or thinking I was never going to measure up. It sucked. It made it hard for me to enjoy my job and extremely hard to focus on anything but the highest expectations of myself. All I could think was about how I was working at the White House now and I should have it all together. The "shoulds" came back. I should have the perfect guy that measures up to Mom and Dad's standards. I should have the perfect body. I "should" have everything!

September 11th changed some of that thinking. I came to the White House early that morning to work on a briefing I was doing for a Presidential event to be held later in the day. The briefing needed to be done by 8:30 am. Knowing I was in danger of missing the deadline, I called Izzy, my supervisor from the campaign, and he told me not to worry, the event was likely not going to happen. My Dad then suddenly called me from his office down on Pennsylvania Avenue and said, "Did you see this?" I ran over to the televisions in my boss' office as the interns, who were just starting their first day, were standing in shock watching the images on the screen. My Dad and I stayed on the phone together as we watched the second plane hit. He said, "That's a terrorist. This is bad." I ran back to my office and he called back five minutes later, "Get the hell out of there. You guys are next." I was gone in a blink. I grabbed my bags and yelled for the interns to all follow me. We ran down the stairs and out the side of the building only to get slowed down at the gate by a group of sweet old ladies who were volunteering. I kindly but forcefully asked if they could get out of the way because we have a life to live! I looked up and saw a plane flying abnormally. The Secret Service agent standing there said, "You better move. That is coming right for us." We went through the gate and took off down the street. I ran up to my Dad's office together and stood at his office window as we watched the Independence Day-like chaos below. I could not believe my eyes, cars on the sidewalk, people running everywhere frantically, helicopters flying low, and then ahead of us, above the skyline was the smoke billowing from what seemed to be the Pentagon. The next plane had hit. The towers then fell in New York City on the television screen. We watched, as everyone did across the country, in shock, as everything unfolded. Who would have thought such a strategy could strike our country? I was also there the next day at 7am when the President I knew and loved showed up and shook every one of our hands to sincerely thank us for being there that day. He told us we would get through it. I was there at the epicenter of our country's power to see our country come together in harmony. It was powerful and moving. I could not help but want to give back myself. I wanted to help these people that were going to come on board from my home state of Pennsylvania with Governor Ridge who needed some help doing outreach. Who else felt the call? Ironically, close to this time, my Dad got a different kind of call to serve; unbeknownst to me it would be a call that would trigger my old fears and insecurities.

President Bush had called my Dad and asked him to serve as Ambassador of Luxembourg. As he told me about it, the place sounded perfect for him. It was small, about the size of Rhode Island, very Catholic, very business-oriented, and lots of military history including the Battle of the Bulge. Luxembourg also loved America. I knew he would shine. I also knew in my heart, I feared losing him again. It escalated my stress. I felt insecure in Washington, D.C., without Dad. I'd spent all this time in South Bend, then Texas. I was finally home in D.C. near our family and my whole family was leaving. I was heartbroken, but I was also happy for Him. That is also the same time I was asked to go into a more stressful part of the White House, Surrogate Scheduling. This job would require me to help send officials of the highest levels of government out across the country. Little did I know that the combination of Dad leaving and the stress of the job would trigger an explosion with my Unhealthy Voice that thankfully was I see a sign from my Healthy Voice telling me it was time to get out of politics!

What Was Going on Beneath the Surface

Just like I said about the campaign, it didn't matter how amazing this job was or how powerful these people were that I was working alongside—I still had this nightmare of an Unhealthy Voice. I hadn't figured out that I had it yet. When I took that job in Surrogate Scheduling, I would call Dad in Luxembourg and he'd say, "This is great! You have to do this. It's for the country," and I'd get all pumped up. I was totally set. Dad and Diane had set me up with this great apartment overlooking the entire D.C. skyline in Northwest. I got to have my own office. I had my own intern and a job that seemed to be pretty great. But it was extremely high-paced, high-level and intense. From managing multiple spreadsheets for the activity of every cabinet member and senior staffer, to navigating hundreds of speaking invitations and who would go in the place of the President as well as memos for cabinet secretaries and White House Senior Staff—you didn't know where your head was half the time. It definitely had its fun days but my Unhealthy Voice was having a field day with it.

Of course my coping habits and behaviors hadn't changed. I had my ways of dealing with stress and they just continued to progressively get worse. The running became my sole focus and enjoyment. It also became the one thing that would carry me through the stress and chaos of the job, which seemed like a good thing at the time but also not a good thing. I can remember one of my office mates walking down the hall with me as I was going out for run one day. He said, "Still running huh? So what are you running from?" It hit me. I didn't know. I knew it was something. I just didn't know it was my own self.

Anything I could do to avoid my insecurities and fears I would do. I was running but I was also going out partying and like I had always done in the past, the drinking was having consequences I couldn't control. The more of them I had, the more I hated myself. The funny part is, I still had the Unhealthy Voice thought that it was a willpower problem, nothing more. So I just focused on running. The marathon training became the excuse for me to isolate from friends, to eat anything I wanted that was "healthy" and to control my drinking. It worked for a while until those times I overate or did choose to drink. I'd often find myself in places I didn't want to be at 4am on a Saturday night. It didn't matter that I was in training or ran 20 miles that morning. My disease knew how to get me. It wanted me to think the answer was outside of me. It wanted me to think that the drink, the food, the run, or some guy was going to be the fix for me. I would do this over and over again on weekends until my self-hatred just got worse and worse.

The crazy part is that I answered this call for a Healthy Voice with an Unhealthy Voice. I gave my body a diet, because that's just what we do, right? I knew there was a White House Weight Watchers group. So I joined. I thought I had it in the bag and my running would help me drop the weight if I just did this point system right, but I wasn't getting the results I wanted as fast as I wanted them. Here I was achieving success by running marathons, working at the White House, and it still wasn't working. Other women were dropping weight and I was doing these marathons, for what? I felt extremely defeated when the women that led the group told me that I couldn't be what they call a Lifetime Member because I hadn't reached what they considered my goal weight.

I felt good with the number and confident as an athletic woman, but all it took was the sweet Weight Watchers leader bringing me right back to my 10-year old self getting on that same scale. She gave me that shaming look and said, "No, sweetie you can't be Lifetime. You've got about 15 more pounds to go until you can do that." I wanted to break something. I couldn't believe my self-worth was being minimized to this little number, but I went with it, and drove myself harder into thinking my weight was the problem more than ever.

Thankfully God graced me with a wonderful guy in my life around this time named Neil, who I'd known since the campaign. I'd just never noticed him because I was too busy looking in the wrong direction at the guys that were bad for me. He loved me and was a blessing. Unfortunately, he didn't have the strength to overcome my Unhealthy Voice like I wished he could have. Only God could do that. Instead he loved me just how he could and got me through the storms at the end. The storms consisted of panic attacks on almost a daily basis. They were sometimes at work first thing in the morning after my Starbucks coffee and staff meeting. Sometimes they were sitting on the couch with Neil watching television. They were absolutely unnerving. When they happened at work, I would have to excuse myself and sit in the bathroom for 10 minutes until they passed. Alternately, my boss would take me down to the White House Infirmary, so I could get some answers from doctors. I often thought I was having a heart attack. Sometimes, Neil would come down from his office, sit with me, and play classical music as the panic attack passed. Everything I was doing to try and control my life—from the diets, to the marathons to the job—everything was falling apart at the seams. Finally, it reached a breaking point. Thanksgiving morning 2003 when Mom was heading down to celebrate the day with us. My stomach went into such a knot; I thought I was having appendicitis. We went to the ER. I got x-rays of everything. We did not know what it could be. The nurse mention something about anxiety but I thought, "Who me? I've got it all together!" It still amazes me that we didn't think to look at what was going on with my addictive behaviors. I can still think back to how my mornings started. All before my 7:30 a.m. Staff Meeting, I would run 3 miles, drive into work, grab a soy latte at the White House Starbucks and a scone, not even think of how it was setting up my body for a sugar skyrocket every morning. I just thought that running was the cure to all my unhealthy woes.

The beauty in this Thanksgiving debacle was that it gave my family and I the tools to go a little deeper beneath the physical surface. We got more knowledge, not answers, but knowledge. After a brutal colonoscopy and endoscopy with a Gastroenterologist I found out more about my insides. He explained why I was getting a feeling in my esophagus like a switch was turning on and my heart was going into overdrive. He said it wasn't my heart but something called Hiatal Hernia where my stomach was protruding out like a bulge above my actual stomach into my esophagus where food could get caught. He said it was probably caused by some sort of bingeing or overeating for long periods of time. (There's the bell!) It totally made sense given the way I had devoured food all my life! Then he said the pain in my lower cavity was from something called Irritable Bowel Syndrome (IBS). He said I carry my stress in my intestines so I was going to have to be careful about my diet and figure out what to eat. I thought to myself, "Aren't you supposed to tell me that?" I had no idea just how little the stomach doctor would help you navigate the journey of life with IBS. Then he said that might also be caused by an allergy to lactose and if I wanted to check that out I should literally "go home and drink a gallon of milk and see what happens." Seriously? I already knew what would happen. I'd be back here in severe pain. No need to test that theory.

The other thing I learned was how interconnected our body is to our mind. A lot of what was going on was with my mental health, which was obvious because of my panic attacks. So Dad found me a therapist that used Cognitive Behavioral Therapy in treating patients. It's a form of psychotherapy that emphasizes the important role of thinking in how we feel and what we do. This work would not only help me overcome my panic attacks but it would revolutionize how I approach my thoughts and behaviors forever. It was a blessing to finally be able to get to a real substantial piece of my mental health as part of the equation. The only hiccup was that I wasn't being honest with him about my behaviors. All I was concerned with was getting the panic attacks and my weight under control. My behaviors with drinking, running and eating weren't something we really addressed.

There is one scripture passage I wish I had known about back then. It would have helped me to know the power of God's word. I hope if you are struggling with anxiety or panic like I was maybe it helps you:

> *"Do not be anxious about anything, but in everything, by prayer and petition, with thanksgiving, present your requests to God. And the peace of God, which transcends all understanding, will guard your hearts and your minds in Christ Jesus."*
>
> —*NIV, Philippians 4: 6-7*

Flash back to the office. All of this inner turmoil was telling me it was time to leave the White House. I did some soul searching to find out what I truly wanted to do and I just knew it wasn't staying in this world of politics. I had a big heart for people and I wanted to help them live a better life. At about the same time, the issue of obesity was hitting the national news like crazy. The President was passionate about fitness and promoting health but because of the war on terror, it just wasn't a priority, but it was mine. I went over to Luxembourg to visit Dad and told him I wanted to work on obesity. Like any good Dad, he would have preferred I chose something easier and better paying, but my heart was way too big for people that suffered from this issue. I had felt empty for so long working in this area of general politics. It was a cool experience, but I wanted to go deeper into my own passion. I wanted to live on mission. I went back and I went over to Karl's office in the West Wing. I said, "I want to go to the Department of Health and Human Services (HHS) to do something about this obesity epidemic because I was that obese kid."

It didn't take long for things to happen. Before I knew it I was in the West Wing with my Mom for my customary "Departure Photo" in the Oval Office with the President. This was my time. I knew the President wasn't going to be able to fight on this issue, but I wanted him to know that I would do it for him. Just before walking into the Oval, the President had just been briefed on the late breaking news that the Pope had died. I walked in, head held high, wearing my bright burnt orange suit, and a Hermes scarf Dad had bought me for the occasion. "Go out on a high note," he said. As I shook President Bush's hand for the photo, he asked me what I was going to do next and I proudly said, "Sir, I'm going to HHS to do something about childhood obesity." He was thrilled. "Good, we need more leadership on that important issue." I was pumped.

Much like my time in Austin, Texas—my time at the White House is precious to me, not just because of the people who came with me from Texas, but because of the memories that we created and the battle wounds we have from being there on September 11th and in it's aftermath. Whenever I hear someone remark about how terrible the White House was run under Bush during that time, I just smile and nod. For me, that time was sacred and those people are my family, not only that, I deeply admire the man who led our nation during those attacks. I still do today. He is a good, loving man, a wonderful father, husband, son and patriot. He's got a huge heart for people that many never see, and that's what I love about him. I'm incredibly grateful I got to experience it all up close because no matter what people say about the politics, it never was and never will be about that for me.

CHAPTER FIVE:

Hearing my Healthy Voice through my Passion for Obesity

My Late 20s

Taking a job at the United States Department of Health and Human Services (HHS) was going to be the answer to my prayers, or so I thought. I thought now that I had a passion for my career the answers would come and everything would be just fine. I'd go to my new job and be able to change the world with what I found out about obesity. The problem was I didn't find out all the answers. I found out that the government didn't have all the answers and I thank God today that they didn't or else I'd still be fighting them thinking they did. I am so grateful for my deep passion and for my Healthy Voice telling me that before I go taking on the world I needed to find out what the government was doing about the issue. I learned so much.

My Search for Answers in Government

My heart was heavy having just left the cocoon of the White House and working for Karl. I felt determined to achieve my mission though. I had a big agenda. I was going into every agency of government I could to tackle childhood obesity and find out what they were doing about it. I was ready to hit the National Institutes of Health, the

Centers for Disease Control, the Department of Agriculture, and the Department of Education. I was not going to leave a stone unturned. Someone should have reminded me I was a political appointee entering the maze of federal government career bureaucracy. I was a little fish in a big sea. I did not know where to go or how to navigate my way, but it didn't matter. I went anyway. Looking back, I see how different I must have appeared. This was not just a job for me. It was a personal mission. I was jumping out of my skin with ideas and yet many of the people I worked with did not share my passion. They were just doing their jobs. Many of them had multiple degrees in medicine, research, and academics to which I couldn't hold a candle. It made me insecure at times, but it didn't stop me.

I got assigned with restarting the working group on Healthier Children between three federal agencies—the United States Department of Agriculture, the United States Department of Education, and HHS. This gave me the authority to find out what the agenda was to address childhood obesity within each of these agencies. I got to talk about it with passion and say, "I was that girl who struggled with my weight and that is why I am here." What I found to be the common denominator was a repeated theme—activity and nutrition. Activity and nutrition! These will fix the problem, but I knew they weren't fixing mine alone! I was listening for something more. I was listening for my missing piece. I got to know every research, community outreach, prevention and treatment program that the government was running. We would meet every month. As the person on the other side of the street, I wanted to hear all of them sending the same message. "We are FOR you, not AGAINST you." I tried and tried but I couldn't get everyone on the same page. I'm not sure what I was thinking trying to do that across three federal agencies, but I am my father's daughter. As my old boss used to say about him and I see in myself, we're like ships that never let our sails down. When I couldn't get them to get on the same message, I tried to get them to get on the same page and find research correlating why working out and eating right is good for kids' academic performance. Despite the fact all these agencies had a seat at the table, there was no movement forward. I felt like I was a part of government inertia. Thankfully, the agency was moving the ball forward in other ways. We rolled out the Secretary's Prevention Award events and developed a book, "A Healthier You," presented by the Office of Disease Prevention and Health Promotion. I was a part of these projects and present at any government event that had to do with childhood obesity in Washington, D.C., including the myPyramid.com launch at the Department of Agriculture. I was in the middle of everything. But I was not fulfilled. I did not want to be in the middle of it. I wanted to change kids' lives like me.

I reached out to a friend, Alicia Moag-Stahlberg, who was running Action for Healthy Kids, a national grassroots organization she founded. She was passionate like I was about the cause and so I knew her heart would be in doing something for the kids. I will never forget riding in a cab with her, telling her my idea. I told her I want to bring the resources together of the different members of the government agencies I was working with and combine them with state programs along with state leaders on the ground. It would create an initiative across the country in which kids learn firsthand about nutrition while they are on the move. When it successfully launched, it was one of the hardest but most rewarding projects of my career. It still runs today at the national and local levels. We pulled it off despite mountains of government paperwork and bureaucracy across the three agencies. It's called Game On! The Ultimate Wellness Challenge and it was hosted right on the National Mall. Busloads of kids with t-shirts were driven in for multiple obstacle courses and learned about how to eat right and how to get moving. Government officials showed up, lunches were provided, and the kids had fun while learning important lessons. It was a success. Of course, what did I notice? I noticed those few kids who did not want to participate. They were the ones I was doing this event for and that day those were the only kids I saw. These kids were struggling with something else, something like I struggled with too. I did not know how to reach them yet.

During my second year at HHS, the obesity issue really started to get a lot of press. Consequently, it was getting a lot of attention. I thought, "Finally! Maybe things will change!" Nothing much changed except what you would except from the inside of government. More cooks in the kitchen at every level of government from top to bottom, more working groups to pontificate on the issue and more people in private industry floundering with what they could do to address it so they don't lose their bottom line.

At the same time, I met a woman named Melissa Johnson, who would be one of the Healthy Voice people in my life. She ran the President's Council on Physical Fitness and Sports for department and she was another passionate person. Our friendship and passion for the cause that we planted at HHS would run deep for a long time and I didn't know it yet but she would be a huge part of my life, especially when I'd lose my Dad. We hosted lots of great events around fitness on the national mall, at the baseball stadium and in a program called Healthier Feds Initiative to inspire federal employees to workout. The coolest part was being able to support her and her team in working with the actual Council to promote the message of activity across the country. I loved that part of my job.

What Was Going On Inside Me

My Unhealthy Voice secretly wanted to finally get the answer on obesity here so that I could stop struggling with my own weight. It may not have looked it on the outside, but on the inside I was still obsessed with my weight. I was still running. I still felt fat. I was still focused on the weight, no matter how I looked. I felt like a failure because I had found none of the answers to obesity in my time here—to think, it was a weight I was putting on my own shoulders. In my personal life, I still wanted to find a guy, still toying with drinking and still running of course. Habits were the same as always, as long as I was looking for my worth outside of myself that's where they would remain.

I decided to dive deeper into the only place I found my worth—my running. This time I put my passion into it by committing to run the New York Marathon for a cause called Team for Kids that created running programs in New York schools to build kids confidence. I reached out to my next Healthy Voice, Michel Edwards, the trainer downstairs in the gym at HHS. I found out he was the running coach for some elite runners. I thought he could do the same for me. He said, "You've got the potential to get a really good time in the marathon." That got my perfect body idea going. We started working out together more often down in the gym. I started running with the fast guys at work. I thought I was making it all happen.

Then it started to show up with the drinking. I remember being in New York with my cousins (the same ones who were with me over the cake when we were kids). Here we were, almost twenty years later and I'm still bringing up the reason why I'm drinking. "Guys, I'm still trying to get over my parents divorce."

I found myself in Nantucket one weekend with my parents while I was training for the marathon the summer of 2006. I was excited because I was getting better time with my running. My friends were up there and they were going to this place called The Chicken Box, a popular place for young partiers on the island. I knew a guy I met earlier was going to be there, so I planned on meeting my friends. I thought, "Just this once. It won't hurt to have one drink." I walked out of there when they closed. I had no control over my body and all it took was tripping over a few stones to break my ankle and set me on an Unhealthy Voice spinout for days. It was this incident that was a defining moment because there was so much at stake with the marathon and in one moment it was all gone. This was when I can say the gene made it loud and clear that it was present. I was so mad at myself, going over in my mind all the things that I had accomplished in my life and I can't just control my alcohol? Nope. I was powerless.

After I tripped, my dream of running the New York Marathon was shattered. The only thing I knew to maintain my weight had been instantly taken from me and the only thing I'd found my self-worth in was instantly gone. I had to have Dad take me to the emergency room to get it set. I had to call my trainer and tell him I couldn't run and I had to have my doctor at home write a note to the marathon saying I wouldn't be running. The running had literally been stopped in its tracks. There was absolutely nowhere to hide or run because I couldn't physically move. Shame kicked in and so did the blame. I asked them, "How am I supposed to find someone to live this life with me when you've got this life here in Nantucket?" I look back and think how much of a Healthy Voice they were on this. They said, "Meredith. You are going to find someone and you guys are going to build your own life together and find your own place to vacation." Then I asked them to tell me what was wrong with me. We came up with the 'only' solution we knew. Dad said, "Well, Meredith. It's got to be your weight." My heart sunk. Total devastation. I'm a failure. It all goes back to the stupid weight—another thing I can't get under control and it's been twenty-five years.

All I could think to myself was, "Seriously, God? Seriously? I am 30 years old now and you still think my weight is not good enough yet? I have a meltdown and you want me to fix my weight?" I had to call Dr. Peeke to set up an appointment. I showed up at her Rockville, MD, office. This time was a bit different. She directly asked me if addiction is in my family to which I said yes. Then, she said, "Well, sister, you've got it with food. You can't pick that stuff up. Someday, you may be able to have a bite of sugar but that time is not right now. You've got to put it down." I thought to myself, "Yes!" It wasn't just a weight issue. It wasn't just a diet issue. There was a bigger mountain to climb.

How God Started to Show Up

Around that time, God started to tug at my emotions in another way. I found out through an email that my best friend, Alexandra Brucker, from Gettysburg had died. Later I found out she'd committed suicide. Here was a girl who I'd only spent one year with of my life but we were soul sisters. We shared similar struggles with weight, self-esteem and our parents' divorce. Now she was gone just like that. It was through hearing this news of someone who truly touched my heart that my heart finally started to break open. I started to feel. I started to think about the amazing influence this person had on my life, even through her struggle. I realized she would want me to let my light shine bright for others.

This is when I started to listen to Christian radio. I started to read Rick Warren's book, The Purpose Driven Life. I felt lost but I needed hope for renewal. I was getting these little nudges to be in relationship with God. I could see him and feel him beyond the church pews. Then, he showed up at work one day. He knew better than me that the answers for me were not going to be found in government. I will never forget where I was when I came to this realization. I was sitting in my 50th panel discussion on childhood obesity at a Washington think tank. Everyone is blabbering on and on how we have to fix the obesity problem with nutrition and fitness. The discussion went to who to blame. It's the parents. It's the schools. It's the government. It's the kids. It's the video gamers. It was like ping-pong and it was a game I had played too long. I was done. I needed to get to those people who suffered as I did and who needed something more than bureaucracy. I heard God say, "Meredith, you are done here. It's time for you to go where the rubber meets the road on the ground. Government is not where you are going to find that." I walked out of that panel discussion and I felt alive. I ran back to my office, called my Dad and told him I wanted to get out of government. I had thought about getting a Masters in Health Promotion at American University, where I had taken some classes. Then, I thought pursuing a Masters in Non Profit would be more fulfilling. I felt like God was calling me for something bigger. I took the GMAT. I also took the time to decide whether or not this was what I really wanted to do. Did I really want to give up everything I had worked for in politics and start a non-profit? Yes, I did. Something was calling me to do it, and I just had to go. I was on my way back to where it all started, South Bend, Indiana. That is where I would really hit bottom and start to finally climb out from underneath my Unhealthy Voice.

CHAPTER SIX:

How Letting Go and Letting God Finally Brought the Light

"Cast all your anxiety on him, because he cares for you. Discipline yourselves. Keep alert. Like a roaring lion your adversary the devil prowls around, looking for someone to devour. Resist him, steadfast in your faith . . . and after you have suffered for a little while, the God of all grace, who has called you to his eternal glory in Christ, will Himself restore, support, strengthen, and establish you."

—NIV, 1 Peter 5: 7–10

This chapter of my life was something of a final frontier. I was going back to South Bend with guns blazing. Since I couldn't fix Washington, I was moving on to a new target. I made the conscious decision to move out to South Bend instead of doing my program part-time over the summer like most of my classmates. I was going to make it work and show my parents I could do this. I had this big dream to build a massive obesity non-profit while I was in school. I was also going to help give Notre Dame a more bustling Alumni presence. I surely thought I was the perfect person to do this since I started the school's Washington Irish Network Group in Washington D.C. God had other plans.

The Drive to Find Answers at Notre Dame

I had a lot of Unhealthy Voices going on around school. I still had fears in graduate school I was not going to measure up. I compared myself immediately to other students and brought back all those voices from my undergraduate years when I had to come in as a transfer. "You aren't book smart. You were never good at math. You'll never survive this." I also received word before I started the program that the Accounting professor didn't want to let me in because he did not think I would get through the program. As you can imagine, I had some serious confidence issues. I also had that insecurity with all these really smart kids in my class who ran non-profits all over the country. Of course my Unhealthy Voice said, "You worked in government. What do you have to bring to the table?" That is why I wanted to change Notre Dame. Clearly, I had set myself up for failure early on with school already. I got a job working for the head of Public Affairs. Apparently, the work wasn't "good enough" for me. When they told me I would have to schedule private planes for people who were coming for event as speakers I said, "No, thanks. I did that on the campaign." I wanted to tell them just how I thought they should make a bigger splash with the Alumni in Washington D.C. Since I was not getting my way, I made another move. I marched myself right into my boss' office and said with an attitude, "I'm done. I just got a job over in Student Development and Welfare at the Athletic Department. I'm going to work on childhood obesity, which is really what I wanted to do anyway." My intentions for the cause were good. My attitude was not. I did not think of the difference between the two at the time. I just kept moving forward with my mission.

The Athletic Department was the next place where I was headed. I walked into the Office of Student Development and Welfare and told them the type of event I thought we should do. It would be modeled after the one I did in Washington, D.C. We could take the athletes into the community as role models for the kids in nutrition, fitness and health. I worked on "Fit for Fun with the Irish" for months. It was an event we would have at both the Parks and Recreation Department and the YMCA to teach kids about nutrition. We would also give them a chance to work out with a Notre Dame athlete by their side. It was a great concept and the event was a hit. Once the event was over, I came up with the same conclusion I did after we held the Washington event. There was something missing. I cannot pin it down. It is not just with the little kids, it is with the athletes, too. I remember staffing the events and the office would teach the athletes about making good choices around drugs, smoking, sex, eating disorders, etc. I just thought to myself, "It feels like there is a disconnect." I, of course, just moved onto the next place, Alumni Relations.

Alumni Relations was the final stop on my multi-office tour of Notre Dame. I was tasked with reaching out to Women and building a group of Notre Dame graduates who serve on boards. It was amazing talking with all of these Notre Dame graduates who wanted to connect. I still felt something missing. I then signed up for a class in the spring semester of 2008 for Entrepreneurship with all the regular MBAs. I was intimidated but I went for it. My elevator pitch got picked. I started it off with, "I was that fat kid you made fun of in grade school." I had a team of guys helping me with the plan and I was on top of the world planning how this business was going to fly and make tons of money. I remember my professor saying my business was going to be the one that took off. I was feeling a confidence I had never felt before.

The Downward Spiral

Through all of this stress with school and work, my Unhealthy Voice was potent. I could do anything I wanted to do, but I was insecure (typical trait of an addict.) As strong as I felt and looked, my Unhealthy Voice still knew it had me here. It knew I hadn't given up my alcohol and my willpower with running wasn't enough to tame it. It knew all I needed was one drink. Things hadn't changed for me since D.C. as far as finding the guy. I was still picking the ones who were going to treat me terribly. At the same time I was training for the marathon, which of course made me constantly hungry. I couldn't get enough carbohydrates or sugar and would live at our grocery store Martin's standing in front of the bakery buying rolls, granola cluster cookies and cereals from the cereal aisle. Hunger was a huge trigger!

My mental health wasn't doing great either. The panic attacks weren't coming back but my anxiety was at an all-time high. Everywhere I go I'd feel like everyone is staring at me. I told my therapist. She sent me to a local psychiatrist. She thought I was having "social anxiety." I was so happy someone might finally know what was wrong with me! I went to meet the psychiatrist and she started to teach me about what was going on with my brain chemistry! First she told me about something called Binge Eating Disorder. All I could hear were the second two words. I never acknowledged I could ever have an eating disorder in my life because I always said, "I'm not skinny enough or, I don't throw up. I couldn't be." I knew I had a problem with food, but I could not have an eating disorder. Here was this woman telling me that I had it. Then she told me about the "Neurotransmitters" in my brain by pulling out a picture of how they function in my brain vs. a normal brain. When the serotonin is low it causes depression, which tells your brain to signal your body to self-medicate with things like food and alcohol. BINGO! I think I said to myself twenty times in my head, "That means it's not just about willpower!" She also told me I have generalized anxiety. She wanted me to try medication. I resisted but given the news she gave me, that it wasn't all up to me—I trusted her as a professional knew better than me. She also gave me something else to try that she thought would help my binge eating. I remember saying, "Yes! Anything to finally get this weight off!" (Mind you—even at this point I still was thinking about getting my weight perfect,) There was a study being run by a graduate student at Notre Dame. She would be leading a group of people selected that struggle with binge eating through the tools laid out in a book called Intuitive Eating by a woman named, Evelyn Tribole. Her intentions were great. Since I was still weight-focused, mine weren't, but it's okay, because I still didn't know the difference yet!

About the same time this was starting, I had just finished the New York Marathon. I met a guy over the phone through Team for Kids that I met at the Expo Booth for the Marathon. Instant fireworks. Things moved lightning fast too. Mom came up for the marathon that weekend from Philly and didn't like it. I was caught up in it and mind you—still hadn't dealt with the root issue! He and I started to date and within a few short months he wanted to move out to the Midwest to be near me so we could try out living near each other. The problem was that he wanted to find himself in me and that was the opposite of what I needed.

This was not a good time for a dependent relationship, as if there is ever a good time. The stress started to snowball. There was the holiday season with all the accompanying food and drinking, the new ways we were asked to start eating with the Intuitive Eating plan, and the stress of my Entrepreneurship class. Add on this new "relationship" and my lack of coping mechanisms or a key foundational relationship with God, and I felt out of sorts. The fact that I was on a Catholic college campus didn't matter much. I was trying to do it all by myself. I was 'managing' it all in my physical body. I thought, "Let me get this food right. Let me get this workout right. Let me get this relationship right. Let me get this school right." Where was God in it? I was doing this Intuitive Eating study to get my eating under control. The opposite occurred. My eating got out of control. My weight got out of control. This study instructs you to drop the food police and intuitively eat your way into a different way of eating. One of the first things they told us was to eat those foods we were afraid of and put them in our house. I had serious terror. She said, "I want you to go get a Costco size bag of M&Ms and put in your house and keep eating it until you are done with it." I remember saying, "I will never be able to stop. I start with those I'll go back and get every other candy and every other food in Costco. I will never stop and I will be 500 pounds." After we talked about it I was okay with trying out some foods I would not normally have tried before. I got back into my cereal, my chocolate covered pretzels, and drinks. I let myself have everything. I started packing on the weight again. I felt like the beast was alive in me, the one that really loved me when I took on the sugar. Despite how hard it was, the method was helping me experience my feelings. It was allowing me to question myself before I ate something and actually feel instead of go right to the food. This was a gift. The problem was I realized how much work I really had ahead of me. I was making progress though and I agreed to be the spokesperson for the study in an article in the newspaper. The paper also took pictures of me running around the local lakes and at the library. I was so passionate about the support group that I wanted to keep it going at the library. I also thought with this publicity, we could invite others to town to come be a part of it. We planned an event for mid-April. I was going to do an online newspaper chat in conjunction with the article to reach more people. I agreed to let the paper interview me including pictures. I was excited to be sharing my experience with those who suffer like I did.

The Final Perfect Storm

The article came out in the *South Bend Tribune.* The headline: Notre Dame Researcher's group gives local Binge Eaters a way out.[8] I looked at the cover of the Health Section. I was cool with it at first but then I didn't like it and didn't know how to deal with my feelings around it. The images are what took me down. One was a drawing of someone stuffing a handful of cereal, one of my old binge foods, into their mouth. Then, above it was a tiny little picture of me smiling. Then inside there was a half-page full body length picture of me in spandex tight pants. The Unhealthy Voice screamed with horror at me, "You are still fat you idiot. It's your weight stupid. It will always be your weight. You screwed up." Now, even worse, it was in plain sight for the entire world to see. I remember calling the newspaper and yelling at them. The author said the editor was afraid people wouldn't know what binge eating was so he wanted to draw a picture. Seriously? I remember talking to Dad about the story and how I liked what it said but really disliked the pictures. We, of course, had a lot of experience with what the media expected. So if that's what it did, then I had to let it go. I went into the newspaper later in the week and did an online chat around the topic of the article. I watched as these people poured in questions about binge eating disorder. I was overwhelmed with hope for all these people who needed help like I did at the beginning of this. Then I was struck by what felt like rejection when I heard the graduate student who led the study respond to a question about 12-step programs around food and how they don't work. Inside, I felt upset not even knowing that would be in my future. I just knew I needed people and other people's stories were getting me through this. That Unhealthy Voice that barked when it saw the picture inside the paper wasn't done beating me up yet.

A few days later, my friend Molly was getting married in the Basilica on the Notre Dame campus. It was the kind of wedding every girl from Notre Dame dreams of having. My defenses were down and my comparing Unhealthy Voice was in full effect. I was going into the Basilica. This was a place where I had not felt God in ages. I would be at a Notre Dame wedding surrounded by perfect-looking Notre Dame people with their perfect looking families and what's worse is they were all the class behind me. I would be sitting in the pew alone, feeling fat and alone, looking different from everyone who fit the Notre Dame blueprint and giving ultimate power to this obnoxious Unhealthy Voice I couldn't shake that was making Molly's beautiful day all about me and my pity party. "Oh, woe is me I'm never going to get married. Why did all these girls go find the perfect guys? How come I couldn't get my act together? How come I could not find Mr. Perfect like my roommates? Why am I such a total screw-up?" I took my pity party to the reception and I ate not the first, but the second meal of my evening. I was afraid I would not have enough food for the half-marathon I was running the next morning. What I did not realize is that the meal I had before the dinner was one of my absolute worst trigger meals, the pre-race pasta meal that I'd had so many times before a run. I thought whole wheat would be better, but it did not matter. Pasta was like a drug to me. I could never get enough of it. It sent my sugar skyrocketing and made me hungrier than anything I could imagine. The worst part was I had eaten a whole box of it. The race was the one thing I was hanging onto by the skin of my teeth at this point as my self-worth. At least I could tell people I was running a half-marathon in the morning and I was pursuing a graduate degree. It really did not matter one way or the other. I spent that entire night saturated with the Unhealthy Voice in my mind. All I was hearing was "I'm less than, not good enough. Everyone here is better than me." Eventually it came time to leave and God gave me the strength to get up the next morning to run the race.

I regretted everything I had eaten the night before, and the way I acted. I hadn't even had a drink. I now hated myself and I did not feel good enough. I ran the race with my stomach in a total mess from everything I had devoured. I rewarded myself for running the race with more food. I went to the Farmer's Market and got myself a soft Amish Pretzel and some cookies. I was still so hungry and I then went over to the Italian Market. I walked through the store and went right up to the bakery case in the corner. It was filled with everything you could imagine in an Italian Family Market, focaccia, lasagnas, cookies, and Danish. It just goes on and on. I stood there with the most intense craving I could ever imagine. The hunger inside me was insatiable, so much that I thought I could eat everything in that case and more and none of it would ever be enough to satisfy my deep hunger inside. My Unhealthy Voice felt like it had taken over my entire being. It was in my heart, my mind, and my soul. Any sense of control I thought I had before over my food or anything else was gone. My willpower wanted to plow through everything in that case. I wanted to reach behind and eat it all right at that very moment, but it was God's will and grace that brought me beyond it. I said to myself, "What the hell is going on with you?" and somehow walked out that door without buying a single thing. I knew God gave me the strength to stand literally in the face of that fear and temptation. In that moment I had reached my point of brokenness where I was completely powerless over the food and began the surrender.

The Moment of Surrender

If you've ever heard the song, "Moment of Surrender" by U2 off their album No Line on the Horizon, then you can feel your way into what all of this was leading up to at this moment.

This surrender moment is when God started to show me the way out of the chaos and into the light. I wanted to be in a place where I would never have to make my life about my weight again. I don't know what brought me to that thinking, only that it had to be the power of God. I was done thinking that my weight was the problem and I was ready to turn it over to Him so He could show me the way. The gifts I would be given in this part of the journey were exactly what it took to make me realize my life was unmanageable and I needed some help. This wasn't something I could do with physical strength. I certainly couldn't do it with my own mind because I desperately needed to get out of my mind and above all, my spirit was completely hardened. He knew I needed Him in that moment more than I knew it myself.

That's when I felt the presence of God in the most powerful way I ever had. I was sitting in the chair at my condo just listening for a sign. Then I just felt this overwhelming sense of love and light surround me. I literally felt God release this weight from my shoulders. Then I heard Him say,

I'm here Meredith. I love you and always have. I forgive you for every single drop of everything you've done. You are reaching out to me right now. You don't have to do it alone anymore. I got your back.

I could drop the fight. I could let go of all the burdens I'd put on my shoulders of my weight, the divorce, Notre Dame, my religion, the government, and most importantly, with myself for everything I thought I had done wrong. I could finally drop the direction I was going in and find a new one. I had been fighting so hard for Him to love me and here He was giving me something called grace. I found this scripture later on in my recovery. It summarizes what the Holy Spirit, at the time, may have been trying to say to me:

> *"For it is by grace you have been saved, through faith—and this is not from yourselves, it is the gift of God—not by works, so that no one can boast."*
> —*NIV, Ephesians 2:8–9*

What it felt like in that moment was pure forgiveness and love. What I found out later was the true meaning of grace, that there wasn't anything I could do to make God love me any more or any less. He'd loved me into being and would never stop. It never was about fixing my weight or getting myself good enough. It was about recognizing that in God's eyes I was always more than enough and letting Him take the reigns so I could rest in Him.

> *"Cast your cares on the Lord and he will sustain you"*
> —*NIV, Psalm 55:23*

Know that wherever you are at this moment, whatever you are feeling is exactly where you are supposed to be. There is nothing you have to be right now except present to yourself for the journey.

> *"Man has nothing to do but surrender—in deep trust, in deep love. Don't be a doer, just surrender. Let there be a let-go."*
> —*Osho*

There is a song that really encapsulates this moment and it's called, "Your Love" by Brandon Heath.

PART II: The Program that Changed my Life

"God, grant me the serenity to accept the things I cannot change, the courage to change the things I can, and the wisdom to know the difference."

—*Rienhold Niebuhr*

CHAPTER SEVEN:

Taking the First Steps

Every step of the rest of my journey came directly from a power greater than myself. It's just this time I knew I wasn't in charge. It didn't mean giving up. It meant finally getting what I needed to live.

I picked up the phone to talk with someone I trusted about where I was at and where my relationship with food had gotten. I shared with her because I knew she'd been there in some way, she'd get me. She asked if I felt powerless. I said, "Yes." She told me I'd never have to drink or overeat again. Then she asked me, "Would you be willing to go to any length to change?" With a sigh of relief I said, "Yes," Another weight was lifted. I found myself driving to the bookstore to buy myself what the people of Alcoholics Anonymous call the "Big Book." Every page I read felt like my story with food and with the alcohol. With each page I felt less alone.

"Step One: Admitted we were powerless over our addictions, that our lives had become unmanageable."

This is the first step of the 12-steps. On so many levels I was out of control with trying to manage my weight. My thoughts about sugar, alcohol, and everything else were in overdrive and somehow I thought I could manage it all. On top of it I had no idea who I was or what to do with all the pain, chaos, and shame inside of me. The inside and outside was just way too much for me to handle. I looked like I was put together on the outside by pursuing a graduate degree and running marathons but I had the emotional maturity of a child. Plus, I thought I was fat and I was sick of feeling fat. I wanted to run away from my life when I felt fat. I dreaded that phone call to my parents, especially my Dad. I had made him so proud for so long. Now, I had to shatter that veneer and tell him that I was falling apart on the inside. I knew it would break his heart. Dad responded like he had to every step of the way in my life with the most unconditional love I could have asked for, like the love of God the father.

I'll never forget the call. I was driving into Chicago along Lake Shore Drive for an Alumni Association meeting at the Notre Dame Chicago office.

I said, "Dad, I need to get away."

He said, "Okay Mere. What do you need? You want to go to a spa or something?" (Oh, how I wish!)

"No Dad, I need some help. You know that addiction that runs in our family? Well I've got it."

He said, (with the grace that only my Dad, having been through it with loved ones could give) "What do you mean?"

I said, "Well, with the food."

Then we started talking and I admitted everything. He said, "I don't understand. You are the most put together girl I know," to which I responded, "No, I am not. That's the whole thing! I'm dying on the inside. I'm a mess. I am put together on the surface but I can't function on the inside!"

Then, he said, "Okay, we'll figure this out. Where do you want to go? Check some things out and then let's talk."

My Dad always loved a project, especially when it came to me. This time I was willing to do the footwork. I knew what I needed to do. We ended our phone conversation with feelings of complete love.

"Hey, Mere. We're going to get through this, all right? You think God could have picked a better person for you to call on this? Have I ever let you down? Meredith I love you more than ever and we'll figure it all out."

I cannot imagine what that phone call must have felt like for him. I am sure he felt a mix of overwhelming fear but also immense relief. I learned later on, when I would finally arrive for treatment, he would call my cousin and tell her how much of a relief it was to know that he did not have to worry about me anymore. We never really got to talk deeper about it. I do know he was a very happy man when he left the earth knowing that I was sober and on the path of recovery. I'm grateful for the role he played in getting me there that day and in supporting me through the process.

What's funny is that we had a place figured out for me to go and then I got a call about this place in Florida, which is supposed to be great. It's one of just a few places in the country that treat eating disorders as addictions. The bell went off again. I knew I had the gene. I wanted that. The place was called Milestones in Recovery located in Cooper City, Florida run by a gentleman named Dr. Marty Lerner. As I looked online, I liked the sound of this place. I liked that it was not going to be a hospital setting and I would learn how to prepare for the real world food wise. The program also included yoga. I also liked the inclusion of 12-step meetings every night. I knew after reading the Big Book I was an addict and these meetings would help me.

I called to speak with Dr. Lerner and immediately I felt like I was safe. This man not only had a sense of humor but he understood where

I was in my most desperate moment. I shared where I was with my food and everything else. Then he asked me the most poignant question probably of my life. He said something like, "So what's your relationship with alcohol? Have you ever had any consequences with that?" Bingo. Right then and there I realized that was the source. I do have the gene. I had been trying to cover it up for so long by running, but I couldn't control something I couldn't control. This guy had just called me out on it. I was terrified but utterly relieved at the exact same time. Then I realized the big one. The food and the alcohol just went together and the food was the gateway drug for my disease as a kid. All of that in one phone call. He told me to read a book that would impact my life in a huge way called, "Anatomy of a Food Addiction" by Anne Katherine that would help me make sense of all the different aspects of this thing. What a blessing in my life.

A Note to You:

You may be reading this and thinking this isn't you. You may also be reading it thinking this could definitely be you. Don't freak out. Just keep reading. Try to be with yourself in the moment. If you have revelations, write about them and share them with a friend you trust. Don't expect to know everything right now. Remember, this is not a fix! If you are open to the journey, you will find the way. Whatever the path, yours is your own. We all have a way we take to walk through change. I honor yours. Wherever you are, just be as present to yourself as you can be!

CHAPTER EIGHT:

Walking Through the Change

God gave me the courage to take the necessary steps to prepare for treatment. He gave me the strength to finish out my semester of business school and pitch a business plan to a panel of entrepreneurs on an obesity consulting company. He gave me the courage to quit my job in the Alumni Association. He also gave me the courage to stand up in front of a group of women I'd organized at the South Bend library to talk about the Intuitive Eating program and be honest. I had to say, "This program helped me separate the food from the feelings, but I've got a lot of deeper work to do and if I'm going to help more people, I've got to go help myself." I just kept walking in faith trusting he would carry me through. I got on a plane for Cooper City, Florida, on May 12, 2008, for my first day of in-patient treatment at Milestones in Recovery. He gave me a little sign with a song as the car was pulling into the treatment center. The song on the radio was Feelin' Good by Michael Buble. As he sang my smile started to smirk up and I just sung along in my heart I knew all was going to be okay. I had walked through the doors. I was not scared. I trusted God.

Meeting Nikki

God started giving me more gifts. He introduced me to Nikki Glantz, RD, LDN. I was really worried about letting someone else into this world. My Unhealthy Voice would tell me, "Excuse me, that is my department." Ha! Then I met Nikki. Her personality and sense of humor immediately puts you at ease. Nikki made you feel as if you were walking through the hardest part of your journey with the best person you possibly could. The work with her would be the game-changer for me. She would provide a new path for me that would allow me to walk down a totally new road helping me navigate food, weight, and exercise. It took my control of the food and exercise off the table and into the hands of God. What a gift. This gave me a new sense of freedom. Taking it off the table would allow me to enjoy foods that nourished me and get creative with those without having to make myself nuts. At the same time it allowed me to address the deeper issues I never could when I was in the food. It wasn't a diet. It was a "Food Plan." It was a roadmap for treatment and Milestones and still is my roadmap for life. It was a new way of living. It felt so good to just let go and say, "Okay, thank God I don't have to deal with this anymore!"

Getting the Plan

Nikki would talk through the plan with me. First, she would tell me what would not be on The Plan. There would not be any processed foods or anything with sugar or flour. Those are the foods that set off a strong reaction for me in my mind and body. The Plan would include real proteins, carbohydrates and healthy fats. It would be based on simple whole foods. When I was learning this I found it amazing how simple it truly was to eat this way. I thought about how over obsessed we've become in our society with the idea of what to eat and here it was—a simple plan. We'd be measuring and weighing out portions so we'd get proper nutrition that kept us fueled. That meant that I wouldn't have to worry about those pesky cravings, because here's the shocker: I'd actually be giving my body what it needed instead of starving it with a leaf of lettuce or a sugar high replacement for a meal.

Then we got to the exercise. She asked me how much I was running. I knew this was coming. I told her honestly. I watched her lips as she said something along the lines of, "Okay, well you are not going to run here." Gulp. One day a time I could do this. I knew doing this now was for the long run because it would help me change my relationship with exercise so I wouldn't have to use it as an escape anymore. It's part of why I was here. I was surrendering it. If they hadn't taken this behavior, I could have left and gone right back at it. But they knew it was right there with my food and I am immensely grateful for their attention to it. The best part is that they were realistic. They didn't say, "You aren't working out at all." They knew as a human being I needed to exercise. They gave me a workout buddy, who consequently also struggled with over exercise so we helped each other walk through this change. They also gave me guidelines of 20-30 minutes, 3-4 times per week without running. Just like the food, I had to get creative. What it did was allow me to bring variety to my workouts, take the power away from how long or how much and find true enjoyment in it. I can honestly say the relationship I have working out today is far healthier. It keeps me grounded and balanced and connects me with my body and mind. It is a gift of life that I cherish.

Putting the Plan into Action

From shopping for food to putting it on the table, I was navigating a new adventure. But it was the best learning experience I ever could have gotten because it's where I feel the most grounded. We were given a binder of recipes and the foods we could eat along with our food plan. For our first visit, we were given a buddy. My first trip to the store was my very first day. We were looking for products without sugar or flour in the first ingredients and let me tell you, the list of ingredients that fell under those two categories was very long. I was amazed how few foods weren't totally processed. I knew the outside aisles were the place to be, but not like this. I was so used to reading for fat, calories, carbohydrates and more. It used to make me crazy. Now I could just look at the ingredients. My life was so simple! I felt like I had the secret ingredient to the special sauce of life! Coming home was a whole other scenario because you had roommate. You had to prepare your own meal and make sure it was weighed or measured. You were also preparing your meals for the next day at the center so you didn't have to worry about that which was great. But the fun part was learning new recipes from your roommates. It was an individual and team effort of learning how to cook in recovery from our eating disorders. The coolest part is that everything was really good! I wanted to share it with everybody! This new way of doing things made me accountable, not stressed. It caused a little anxiety to plan but I knew I now had a plan to eat healthy!

The Relief the Plan Gave Me

The Food Plan cleared my mind and my body did not feel bloated. I started to notice the disease was not running around like a dictator in my mind. Of course, I had cravings. Who wouldn't when you were chasing them for more than twenty years? Then, I would realize my body was getting everything it needed. Physically, I loved it. I felt good in my body. I could taste my food. I slept better and I was not dieting or trying to run off my calories! I was also exercising moderately, for 20-30 minutes a day. That was enough with the food I was eating. I was blown away. How deceived I had been for so long. Did I want to run? Of course! I kept pushing through and sticking to the plan though. I was committed to the bigger picture, to myself, and the journey, rather than pushing for the finish line. I sure did have my moments where I wished I could escape, but that was the blessing of being in a treatment center. I had medical support, emotional support, and friends who were walking the same path with me going through the same stuff. I was finally coming out of this isolation with my disease and dependence on it. I was finally finding my Higher Power and the light.

Embracing a Spiritual Program

The 12-step meetings I was attracted to when I first found the place were something that became a huge part of my healing. Without that spiritual program, I wouldn't be where I am today. Ultimately, it was God who brought me out of that darkness so it made sense to me that I wanted to keep walking with Him along the way. Those meetings felt like home to me. The first one I went to, I sat in the back and saw a woman who looked exactly like my grandmother. It was almost as if with her piercing blue eyes that I inherited, she looked across the room and said, "Welcome home Mere." Doing just a food plan would have never worked. Dr. Lerner would say that doing the food plan without the spiritual is like a diet. I knew that had been my own god for too long. I needed a spiritual program to heal my spiritual sickness. I needed to heal my relationship with the God. The "up there, not down here" wasn't there anymore. He was right there with me now. I could feel it.

"Step 2: Came to believe that a power greater than ourselves could restore us to sanity."

Step 2 of the 12-steps and I was starting to realize all those addictions I had used, were things that were never supposed to fill me up. Only He could. This started to bring me peace. I wanted more of it. It felt like I was healing not just my mind and body, but my soul. I really wanted to know more about God. I wanted a relationship with Him. I started to seek him out in people's stories in those rooms. It amazed me how different we all were by appearance and stories but how similar we all truly were inside. These people were helping me believe that God could restore me to sanity because he was doing it for them, and me. This was a way of life, a design for living. I was okay with not graduating because I wanted to keep walking on this path. I wanted to know God was in charge and I was not alone anymore. The longer I stayed with it, the more I trusted what God was doing in my life. I felt comfortable about getting honest about what I needed to get rid of from the past. I didn't want to hold onto it anymore.

A Note to You:

Some of you reading this may already have a spiritual program and this is just a complement to it, a reminder of how far you've come on your journey. If you haven't gotten one—do you realize the potential of bringing a power greater than yourself into this, of giving that power the ability to handle what you can't? I know it is hard to believe. You think you cannot control the food. We have been taught our whole lives "you should keep it under control." That's because we've separated our physical selves from our spiritual selves. We've not realized how much the spirit of God is within us to strengthen us where we are weak. What if you asked Him to be with you in your weakness and to make you strong in the face of it instead of asking him to take it away?

CHAPTER NINE:

Learning More about my Addiction

I went to treatment for an eating disorder and I got treated for cross-addiction. That means they didn't pick one substance to focus on but they went right to the root. They grabbed my disease by its neck and did triage at every corner it was trying to get me. By looking at the addiction itself, I was able to stop focusing on the food or the alcohol, which were but symptoms and focus on myself. It also gave me the ability to recognize my addictive personality. So that yes, food, alcohol, and running maybe the "drugs of choice" for my addiction, but really anything I do that's addictive is my disease trying to creep back into my life. My disease loves to be in black and white. The trick is finding the middle way with recovery and my Higher Power as my guiding light. This knowledge allows me to be more present to myself in any circumstance. It gives me the ability to step back and look with compassion instead of criticism. I can say, "Oh! There's my addiction, and leave it at that." That is truly a gift.

It is one thing to go to treatment for an eating disorder and another thing to go to treatment for a chemical addiction. There are not a lot of places that treat the addiction itself, especially addressing both eating and alcohol. I know food was the gateway drug for my alcohol. If I choose one, I had to choose the other. I also know that if I were to just treat my alcohol I would go back out and dive into another eating disorder. It was like my disease was a mouse that never wanted to be trapped. I am grateful the staff at Milestones knew it needed to be trapped from every angle so that when I got back into the real world I could identify it from every aspect.

This is why when I see articles about whether or not food addiction is real, I chuckle. It seems that this topic is becoming as prevalent as obesity did back when I started at HHS. I am one of those people as they say in recovery, "resigned from the debating society" on this one. It's already in the bag for me. I can tell you the minute I realized it, and remembered the gene was in my family—it just clicked. I chose to do something about it. You can too. Believe me, the reporters will keep writing about it, scientists will keep researching it and many people will keep debating it, just like they do the disease of alcoholism. It's a free country! Yet, on a subject like this that is about my truth? I'm not going to debate. We all have our own truths and what works for us. Believe me I've been challenged by experts to come up with the scientific evidence. It did not matter. I was the evidence. There were thousands of people outside that room that were the evidence too. I did not need psychologists to tell me this could not be my truth. It was my truth. This was way past anything psychological for me. The game for me was spiritual now and I was fine with that. I thank God I couldn't think my way through my mess.

A Note to You

We are not just physical beings. We are spiritual beings and emotional beings. We are also people who were handed down from generation bodies and brains that we didn't choose but we have to work with everyday. It's up to us to figure out how we are going to approach our life walk with them. Are we going to be the victim or are we going to take action? Are we going to pretend that our mental health is something we don't have to address? It's something we can handle alone? Or are we going to finally look at it seriously? It takes what it takes. There comes a time when we need to stop giving our power away to what the world thinks we should do with our health and figure out what we need to do with it to get it back.

The Physical Part

Every week, while working on getting off my drugs and finding a spiritual path, I learned from Dr. Lerner and the people at Milestones what this was all about. I will tell you I soon learned two big concepts: this was very serious and I was going to have to learn to live life in a new way.

I remember one day Dr. Lerner drew a line graph. He drew a line going up very fast and high illustrating the reaction when a food addict eats sugar. Then, he drew it going down really fast to show its dissension. Then, he drew a line completely different to show the contrast of a non-food addict's physical reaction to it. It was much steadier. He talked about what the sugar spike does to all of us. Now, I know for me, I started thinking of the foods that would give me that reaction. It was white pasta, baked goods, and milk chocolate. It was anything processed and sweet. Then, I thought how starved I would be after eating them. They never satisfied me. I would then get in my head and become obsessed with eating more. I would either feel fat from eating them or crave them more intensely. It was a total mental and physical craving I could not control. It all stemmed from this physical reaction to eating processed foods and sugar. I was self-medicating my brain chemistry with this every day. This was not about my willpower. Dr. Lerner also talked about our hypothalamus in our brains. This is the control center for quite a few of our brain functions including metabolism, hormone regulation, mood regulation, sleep cycles, hunger cravings, and energy levels. If that is off, I am off. He explained it is like a broken switch and therefore we can't "trust our gut" when it comes to food. All the imbalance wants us to do is self-medicate based on our senses. So, we smell, taste, and see food and we want it. We have no sense of control over it. There is a way to get it under control with proper diet and lifestyle but once you switch into it, you are vulnerable to it. This explains why I need to use a scale, why the world struggles with portion sizes and why Intuitive Eating did not work for me at the time. It also explains why I do not need to beat myself up about this. I'm learning how my physical brain and body reacts when I eat this way. But I also needed to go deeper, to the feelings.

CHAPTER TEN:

Finally Finding the Root: My Feelings

Now that I was not beating myself about the food anymore, it allowed me to do the real work internally. I knew I had the gene and that was how it started. The bigger problem was I was not feeling and I needed to feel. Thankfully, Milestones taught me how to start examining my feelings. It was hard and worth every second. Had I not been in a therapeutic environment to address wounds I was carrying since childhood, I would not have gotten to where I am today. I had to face that initial trauma. I had to go back to my childhood when Dad left, and it was just Mom and I. I had to look at all my reasons for eating and drinking so I could take away all the power I was giving to the pain. I had to let go of my story. I could not fix this pain. I could start the process of peeling the onion to get on the path of healing and growing instead of numbing myself and staying in the same place. This was truly the emotional core of what I needed to work through so I would not have to return to the physical alone to feel good about myself. Walking through this pain would teach me to walk through any pain. Thankfully, God knew I could not do this alone.

Many people talk about their first drink, I talk about my first memory with food. That was my gateway drug to get to the drink, even though I did not start drinking until much later in life. It did not matter. The disease was waiting. It loved that I was using the food at such an early age. It loved that I had a reason to go to it. I had no siblings to lean on, I felt bad about not being able to save my Mom from her pain, and I felt different from all the other kids in class. The disease wanted it to be "just you and me kid." It truly was what we call a disease of isolation. I started to find out how much it had made me believe I was the victim of my parent's divorce. The disease kept me stagnant for 20 years by making me think I had to relentlessly blame my parents for their choices. All the while it kept me from taking care of myself, but I was now. This event was in the past. I was dealing with it right now. I was done with it. It had led me to believe I was a failure. I was not. I know that now. I was just born with a gene into an environment where the gene got triggered by an event that was out of my control. Period. End of Story.

Now that I finally realized I couldn't blame my parents anymore, I had to see them with new eyes. This was really tough. I love my parents very much. I grew up with each of them as an only child and I was always very close to them. They were my best friends. Now, I started to see how attached I was to them emotionally, mentally, and financially. I needed their approval for everything. My life was never about me. It was always about pleasing them. It was a very harsh reality to realize my dependence. I had not grown up yet and now it was time. I started to become more aware of how I was behaving. I loved and admired my Dad for a very long time. I also always blamed him for leaving and for making me so financially dependent on him. I really disliked that about myself. We were so close. One of the ways he showed love was by dispersing gifts. This linked my self-worth with material things. I'll never forget how God helped us start working through this when it was my 31st birthday. Being the princess that I was, I was expected to be showered with presents by my parents. I kept going to the front desk asking for mail. I got a package from my stepmom and brother with an adorable card. I barely paid attention to at the time. I was expecting more maybe flowers from Dad or a package from my Mom. I remember calling them and just unleashing, "Of all times! Now, you don't send one?"

There was the blame and shortly thereafter there was the shame. I threw myself right into a pity party of my parents not loving me and cried my eyes out. My Mom felt so bad but she didn't know what to do in this situation. I remember walking out of the therapy room and my therapist just looking at me seemingly saying, "Have fun feeling this one!" I was screaming at my Dad and crying on the phone while he was pouring out unconditional love. I asked him why he had to buy me all those things for all those years to make me think my worth was in material things. That is when I had a breakthrough.

"Wait, Dad. My worth isn't in the material. God just gave me a gift. This is my crazy thinking that my self-worth is based on the material but God wants me to break through it by giving me less material items to show me that you guys love me no matter what."

"YES! I love you. " He said.

I never went back to where I was then. My worth was no longer in material things, or my happiness. I was not little Meredith anymore. Going forward, I would still have a lot of growing to do regarding those issues. I am so grateful I got to talk through a lot of my time in treatment with Dad. It felt like he was the angel sent to guide me. I loved sharing about our common struggles with the sugar. Dad would say, "That's it! That's exactly why I love the bread at the baked goods!" He, too, would try to quit sugar for a few weeks. When I would come home to visit, he would take me to Whole Foods and still swing by the baked goods case for a treat though. That was my Dad!

My relationship with my Mom was another story. She was my Mom but she was also my soul sister in the divorce. We got through it together. We were so close for so many years. I could not figure out now, why it was not working. I just knew it was not. It was easier to remove myself with Dad because he had his own family. Even though my Mom and I were not geographically close, we were emotionally dysfunctional. I always felt like I wasn't enough in some way, ever since I was a kid. I felt bad for finally taking care of myself. I was afraid again that I was abandoning her, like always. I also felt it my responsibility to help fix her and make sure she was happy and secure, and not hurt. All those years, when it was just the two of us, had set the pattern. I was living my life for her. I did not even realize it. I was using the addiction to escape my "responsibility" of trying to keep her happy. When we are not living for ourselves, we are only making ourselves miserable. I realized I was suffering from years of taking on my mom's suffering. I did not need to do that. I had to start owning mine and letting her own hers. We went through that divorce together but also as individuals and I needed to own my pain. This was extremely tough. I would call her and we would talk about the semantics of my journey. How sugar was harmful for me. Like Dad, she could relate to the ride it had taken her on in her own life.

The tough part for me was getting beyond the semantics, the "safe" conversation. I needed to tell her there was more to it for me than the food. A lot of my cross-addiction issues were things we shared in common. Each aspect of my addiction was a way that she showed me love and we would then bond. There were care packages sent with chocolate and clothes and love. I had to call her and say she could only send packages with love. No more chocolate care packages like she sent every holiday. I had to tell her the things I could and could not do with her. I could only imagine the blow she took. It would have hurt me if I was on her end, too. It hurt me to tell her. It hurt even more to imagine not sharing those things with her, but I just had to trust God. Many of these things were what made our relationship so sweet. What I told her completely cleared the slate and changed the game. I had to do it. I had to tell her, for example, I was not training for marathons anymore. I felt like I was shutting the door to the bonding mechanisms we had established across the years. I had no choice. I had to get healthy and change my relationships. I could not explain it and that's what hurt the most.

I could barely stand how much this might be hurting my Mom, but these were the first steps of starting to become myself. The worst was when I had to tell her my truth about being done with the divorce. I reached a point where I realized the bitterness around it was killing my soul. It had literally made me want to turn to my addictions for so many years. I was ready to move on. This was just about the absolute hardest moment to walk in my life. My butterflies were intense. God gave me the courage. I said, "Mom, I'm done blaming Dad for the divorce. I've got to move on." I remember her response. I had to stand in my truth. I had to let her own her stuff so I could pick mine up and start getting rid of my own.

If I had not done that work, I would not have had the healing I had with my Dad that was crucial to my recovery. Working through these feelings with each of my parents individually was the right course. It is Milestones that taught me how to sit with my feelings. As painful as they may be, I never have to drink, eat or run away from them. I will never forget the moment that I learned this. One day in treatment, I was so overcome with emotion around fear I burst into tears. I wanted to run for the hills, or drink or eat, but I couldn't. So I went into the bathroom and fell to the floor. I then realized, I'm always going to want to run from these feelings. I'm always going to have to feel to grow, and that is okay.

A Note to You:

This is why our feelings are so important to feel. We can't expect them to go away or be stuffed down with food, especially if they've been around for a long time. Do you realize the absolute best thing you can do for those feelings is to feel them? It is okay to feel them! They aren't going to hurt you. They are a beautiful part of your being. If you are too scared to walk through them alone, there are people who can help you do that. You never have to go through them alone if you don't want too. You never have to eat over them again if you don't want too.

CHAPTER ELEVEN:

Preparing for Life on Life's Terms

After six weeks in Milestones, it was time to leave. An exit plan was required to fill out before I left so I could learn to keep living this way with a plan in hand. I was not fixed in treatment and that mindset was in itself, a fix. I had started to do the healing work and I had gotten the tools to start living. In reality, I was just getting started. All I got was the roadmap and some walking shoes. I had been given God's grace. I started working a spiritual program that I could take with me wherever I went. Now, I was going to have to go home, get a sponsor and start working the steps if I was going to live this new way of life. I had heard someone say, "The only thing you have to do is change your whole life." I was ready. I did not want to go back to the person I was and I loved having God in my life. I had tools I had practiced for six whole weeks that was an amazingly long stretch for me. I felt good about my Food Plan, my recipes, my snacks, and my exercise plan. I was not scared of myself. I felt good in my skin. I was ready to go back to school and dive into classes. Milestones told me to only start with one class at a time. Although it was less than I wanted to do, I grew to like the idea. Whatever God wants is what God wants.

I'm not running the show anymore. I also had this great tool to keep me grounded. Dr. Lerner gave it to us when we first started at Milestones. It is called S.E.R.F.[9] It stands for the following:

S = Spirituality

E = Exercise

R = Rest

F = Food Plan

It would help me to stay balanced on the recovery journey.

Leaving that last day was gut wrenching. I was going to miss everyone. I felt like I had found a new family of people who really loved me and understood me. I felt as if I had had been reborn. I was going back into the real world but I was not alone. When it was time to leave I stood up and my therapist asked, "Meredith, are you ready to leave the nest?" What a powerful question to lead me out the door. I was ready. I hugged all my sisters in the room and then headed back to South Bend. I felt so good. I felt prepared for the journey ahead. I knew it was going to be tough. I knew the world was not going to cater to me. I was ready. This time, I had God behind me and six weeks of recovery behind my back. I also had a Food Plan and a schedule of AA meetings to guide me as soon as I got off the plane. I was armed and ready.

Being Aware of the Disease in My Mind

"Do not conform any longer to the pattern of this world, but be transformed by the renewing of your mind. Then you will be able to test and approve what God's will is—his good, pleasing and perfect will".

—NIV, Romans 12:20

I knew now I had a disease of my mind, which was to trying to keep me out of the moment. That was another reason why I needed meetings. I needed to remind myself this life can only be lived one day at a time. I could not let myself get too far ahead of myself. I was not sure at this point if I really wanted to finish this degree or not. When you get into recovery you do not run. You finish what you start. That is what I planned on doing. I was finishing what I started and trusting what God had planned with the rest. I also needed to stay with myself. I could not start comparing myself to other people who could do the things that I could not do anymore like drink or eat certain things. I could not do those things and that was okay. I knew myself better. It helped me to be with myself and allow God to continue to work on my mind.

Being Aware of the Disease in my Body

"Those who live according to the flesh have their minds set on what the flesh desires; but those who live in accordance with the Spirit have their minds set on what Spirit desires. The mind governed by the flesh is death, but the mind governed by the Spirit is life and peace."
—*NIV, Romans 8:5–6*

This would be one of the absolute most important things for me to remember. I am human. I will have desires of the flesh. I will want those things that are material. I will want things outside of me that make me think I'll be better with them. By the grace of God I will receive many of those things. I also need many of them to survive. But none of them can ever bring me happiness. Living in the spirit has given me the grace to know they can't. It is important for me to remember which of those things I have already gone too far with which I thought would fix my body. A workout, a diet, or a drink was not the answer to my problems. I know my limits. I know when I have gone too far and I know where I cannot go. I know this like I know my own name. Any of these things could set me back in my disease. This is why I had to go to treatment to arrest it and find a better way. I am grateful I now choose to use my tools while remaining aware of my human tendency to want things of the flesh. The things I have been addicted to affect me in ways that do not affect others. I cannot handle it like the rest of the world and that is okay. It allows me to be better prepared for the journey.

Realizing my Unhealthy Voice would Trigger Me

There is a term used in addiction and trauma recovery called "triggers." From what I understand, it refers to all the things that make us want to revert back to our disease, crave the old substance, or revert back to old trauma reactions. Not being aware of your individual triggers is what I believe sets many Americans back on their weight-loss or healthy lifestyle paths. They think if they work hard enough these weaknesses will go away. This is the point where so many of us fall backwards. We don't have to. I would find on this journey of treatment, I was given the gift of having multiple addictions in the flesh. It would allow me to empower people like you with many tools to navigate your addictions if they materialized. Learning what triggers me was incredibly important to navigate what makes me want to eat. Overeating and subsequently fixing our bodies with such culturally accepted behaviors, many of us do not realize what triggers us as we walk. We need to since we have to live with food every day. We essentially have to change the way we approach it. What people need is a gentle and honest but loving voice to walk them through the thing that is hands down the hardest thing to navigate in life, an addiction to food. This is not alcohol. We can't be perfect with it. We need a structured plan that works for our individual makeup and we need to be able to adapt when our triggers show their ugly faces so we don't get caught back up in the "It's my body, I'm worthless," mindset.

Food is something we have to use every single day. We all use it differently and have our own roadmaps. We also have our own stories, triggers and physical makeup. So judging another for how they walk their path with it is not wise. We are stronger together if we are present to our strengths and weaknesses on our individual paths. Think of NIV, Matthew 7:1, "Do not judge, or you too will be judged." The best way we can navigate it is to be absolutely honest with ourselves, others and God with whatever food program works for us. Most importantly, learning what our triggers are and being aware of the triggers that face us every day will shape our actions positively. We will know our Higher Power is with us as we face them and we grow stronger as we take this journey.

This is not meant to be a formula for perfecting your relationship with food. It is only a way for you to get accountable with yourself and to know your weaknesses so that they may become strengths.. As you learn about mine, and become aware of your own, do not let your food police, or your 'shame and blame' voice come out. This is not a fear approach. This is a full awareness approach where you become an active witness to your own triggers and behaviors. The best way to do it is if you have a plan that is grounding you so you are not using food in an unhealthy way. Do not worry about that now if you are not ready. Be aware. Your specific triggers will be different than mine. Everyone has their own path. Do not compare! Sharing your journey though, how you walk through it, will help you get stronger in your weaknesses. This is about a gentler, healthier way of life for the journey, not a "fix-you" journey.

"Build up your weaknesses until they
become your strong points."
—*Knute Rockne*

A Note to You:

This is a complete change of thinking from what most of us are used to when it comes to creating a healthy lifestyle. We are used to the fix. We are used to trying to perfect the food, our bodies, or our workout. This is why you are going to think differently. Those programs that help you change in the physical and get you grounded in a workout or a nutrition program are what you need to get you to a place where you can be present to your physical self. What you really need them for is not to give you perfection or the main focus of life, or the perfect weight. You need them to help you navigate the journey ahead. That journey ahead is everyday life. So relieve yourself right now of all the pressures to be good enough in the physical and imagine having a program that will help you be grounded in the physical body so that you can walk through all the kinds of stuff life brings. What you are going to find is that life is so full, it doesn't make sense to focus on that perfect weight anymore. It's about being grounded in your Healthy Voice, and taking care of yourself, knowing exactly what works for you in your whole self! As you read, you'll see how my life was just life—living in the everyday, trying to navigate triggers and then getting through the big and little things. That is exactly why you need a Healthy Voice and why I'm sharing with you what life was like when I got out of treatment those first few years—so that when you do choose a program, you can know that you are just getting started. Let the journey begin!

PART III: Learning How to Navigate Life with Food and Everything Else

"Consider it pure joy, my brothers, whenever you face trials of many kinds, because you know that the testing of your faith develops perseverance. Perseverance must finish its work so that you may be mature and complete, not lacking anything. If any of you lacks wisdom, he should ask God, who gives generously to all without finding fault, and it will be given to him. But when he asks he must believe and not doubt, because he who doubts is like a wave of the sea, blown and tossed in the wind . . . Blessed is the man who perseveres under trial, because when he has stood the test, he will receive the crown of life God has promised to those who love him".

—NIV, James 1: 1–6, 12

CHAPTER TWELVE:

Year One of the New Journey

The Adjustment

Getting back home was weird. I was going into the old environment in a new way. It took some time to readjust the sails. I will never forget calling my friend Patti to see if she could pick me up and saying, "Would you mind taking me in my house? I'll need your help throwing out some food." I will also never forget walking through that door. It was like walking into the set of a CSI crime scene. I knew there was going to be wreckage. That is where I had shut my front door in order to isolate myself and keep the world out. I had wanted to be alone with my thoughts and my food. That is why I needed my friend there. We walked right into the kitchen. We grabbed trash bags and started throwing out all my binge foods. We also threw out anything that had sugar or flour in the first four ingredients. I put up on the wall the vision board I had created at Milestones to keep me focused in the moment. In that moment, that place was a trigger for me because it's where I left my disease. Over time though I would come to nurture it. I would find it to be a safe place in the storms of my early recovery, a harbor for spiritual renewal and a truly Healthy Voice place for me to find peace.

It's amazing what happens when you can change your perspective from fear to gratitude about a space. It took me a long time. I still have my moments with it. But healing there was a direct representation of how I could learn to be with myself.

Walking the Walk

The program of recovery would become my rock. It was my spiritual foundation. I tuned into the principles of S.E.R.F. (Spirituality, Exercise, Rest, Food Plan) and went to work. Outside of meetings, I found my safest place to be the grocery store as I had become so accustomed to navigating it at Milestones. It was so nice to walk by triggers and know I did not have to pick them up or give them any power. The same thing happened for me with exercise. I was doing it for the real purpose of it and not doing it to purge the food or alcohol. I had fun with it. I started doing yoga more and bike riding outside rather than just running. Variety was a good thing! I'll never forget the day I was walking around the lakes with a classmate of mine, a huge milestone for me. I said to her,

"Wow. This is huge. A year ago I wouldn't have been able to just walk with you. I would have been jumping out of my skin thinking I needed to make this count as a run. Now, I can just enjoy a walk with you without obsessing about the intensity, the calories burned, or the distance. This is awesome!"

Rest had even become a part of my recovery in a way. It felt great not to wake up with a food or drinking hangover. I loved going to meetings every week and going to church every Sunday morning. I even found a priest I really liked at Holy Cross College. I was getting into the groove of recovery, but only by not doing it alone. I loved the people walking alongside me. They understood what I was doing and the dark places I had been. They were trying to appreciate life and walk through it just as I was. I felt lucky to have them in my life.

Going Inward: Meditation and Prayer

"Sought through prayer and meditation to improve our conscious contact with God as we understood God, praying for knowledge of God's will for us and the power to carry that out."
—*Step 11 of the AA 12 Steps*

I knew I was not at this step yet but I wanted to connect with God daily. I started reading daily reflections online and in reflection books I had gotten while in recovery. They always connected me to my Higher Power and set me on a positive path for the day. Even better, meditations were giving me a healthy alternative to my old obsession with horoscopes. Instead of seeking the answers to my future or what was going to happen that day, I could be reminded of God's plan. These meditations were helping me see He was bigger than I had ever imagined. He really did love me. He was showing me more each day and that gave me the hope and peace I was always seeking. With each day I let go more of the struggle from the past and the shame I continued to let Him heal me. I started to find that no matter how my day went I would make it through with Him, good or bad. I found God loved me right where I was, no matter what I was going through at that moment. He was in it with me for the long haul. Although I would recognize I'm human and sometimes I'd want to take back my will, he'd always be there to remind me he had my back.

Retraining my Senses

A huge gift in early recovery was getting my real senses back that weren't numbed by the need for false things. The smell of things like donuts and other baked goods felt counterfeit to me now. I craved new sensory experiences. I craved multisensory experiences like being in nature. I felt like it was a whole new world because I could see things more clearly on so many levels. I loved going to the Farmer's Market to buy the fresh, bright colored fruits and vegetables and flower arrangements. I loved watching the tree outside my window as it changed with the seasons. I loved going to the beach and just walking on the sand. Every connection my senses had with the nature felt like it rooted me deeper into myself and brought me closer to God.

One particular time, I was on a Milestones retreat in Stone Harbor, New Jersey. It's a place that I used to go with my family when I was a kid. Mom and I went down a day earlier to recapture some of the memories and catch a nice morning run on the beach. What a gift. While I was there I tried to go to the beach every day. On the last day in the early morning, I decided to take a walk to talk with God. With the sand under my feet, the ocean beside me, the sky above and the air surrounding me, I set out. I could feel His presence. Then I heard Him say, "Remember Meredith, I'm always walking with you. I'm always listening and here for you." I started to well up with tears. Then I looked down and found a special gift at my feet as I went to turn around. It was a big, beautiful conch shell that was the physical evidence of what He'd just said in my heart. I felt at peace and full of love. It was like a live version of the famous Footprints Prayer.

School

All of these things that grounded me and brought me peace in my recovery gave me the physical stamina and clarity to focus on academics. This is something that was never my strong suit. It did not matter. I was not giving that Unhealthy Voice any power. I was going to walk through it no matter how much work it took. I was grateful I had the clarity in my mind as the classes were only getting harder. I had to focus on the goal and the goal was to get my Masters Degrees. I knew my limits and I couldn't party with my classmates or touch the IM chats everyone was doing in the middle of class. I knew it would cause me to lose focus. These kinds of classes, financial management, statistics, and economics did not come easy for me. I was not going to mess it up. I knew not caring was just another way for my disease to creep back into my psyche. No way. No how. I worked really hard and passed my classes.

Purpose

Since school was only part-time, I was able to discover more about what I really wanted to do with my life. I had spoken to Dr. Lerner at Milestones about exploring the world of eating disorders and food addiction. I started scheduling trips to some conferences to check out what was there. I had no idea how I might fit in, but I was passionate. I traveled to the National Eating Disorders Conference in Austin, Texas, and met people who had stories like me who inspired me even more. There was a girl who went to treatment for her exercise bulimia, a woman in her forties that battled bulimia and was writing a book, and a woman who counseled college women. It's also when I met the Founder of the Binge Eating Disorder Association (BEDA). She was a kindred spirit because there weren't many people who were voicing their recovery from the disorder. I was happy she had chosen to use her Healthy Voice by starting the organization and lead the way in the fight. I got to meet another woman who inspired me, named Jennie Schaeffer, an author who wrote, Life without Ed read by many who suffer from eating disorders. I felt called to connect to these people who were using their voice and encouraged them to keep inspiring people with their truth. All of this courage surround me gave me even more courage to stand in my truth.

While I was there, I was reading a book, "Finding Your North Star: Claiming the Life You Were Meant to Live" by Martha Beck, a Life Coach to Oprah and author a few different books about finding your purpose. I read it quickly and found by the end that I not only wanted to write a book, but I wanted to be a coach. I wanted to help people transform their lives from the inside out. This woman's story of overcoming society's ideals to find your true "North Star" blew me away with inner courage. I wanted her to train me and I wanted to meet more people like her. That group of Martha Beck Coaches would introduce me to the process of transformation and so many other things of what it takes to be a coach. Their stories and how they use them to transform others lives truly amaze me. I'm grateful to know them.

Lessons in Responsibility

Sometimes when we have a passion, we want to jump in and have it all work out right then and there. Yet, we still got to pay the bills. I got a job at Talbots to make money and pay for groceries. Guess what I found out? I learned how to be responsible in a retail job. It also triggered my spending. Thankfully I caught it and realized after a few months and a holiday season that it was time to find another job. We live and learn.

Relationships

For the first time in my life, I was able to start navigating what life is all about—relationships. When we're in isolation with our disease, it's the only relationship we have. We don't know how to be with other people or let love in, but these people in the program were teaching me how to love myself. The relationship I was finding with God was guiding the way and giving me faith that all things would work out even if they were tough for a time. Just like my addiction, my relationships were scarred and it would take time for them to heal. I would have to do the work to clean up my side of the street. I would have to find out the true meaning of love and forgiveness, but the healing wasn't up to me. That was God's part. All I could do was pray for the willingness to walk through these relationships and get honest with myself. I had to do this to get out of the isolation. The beautiful part is that the more honest I was, the deeper my relationships became. Trust developed. I wasn't so afraid of getting hurt. I wanted to make things work, and at times I jumped the gun, but I learned from each of those experiences. When emotions ran high I knew it wasn't up to me to fix. God had a plan to work these things out if I'd just trust Him. Those relationships would be the anchor to release me from my shame and isolation.

One of the other gifts I got was a relationship to walk the journey of life. I wasn't looking, nor was I expecting it but I met a guy named Michael. I liked him for who he was in his deepest, most authentic self. He was a good, humble man with a big heart, a good sense of humor, and I liked that. I was done with complicated men. God allowed me to see this man not for his resume but who he was being. We loved being together and had fun. We shared the same values. We are connected from our hearts on a spiritual level which infuses every aspect of our lives together. We found that we loved nature, being physically active, having a relationship with God, and cherishing family—the simple life. In each other, we found what matters most. From that spiritual core we could meet each other honestly with every aspect of our lives. The fact that he was a dad with three wonderful kids and I was a professional woman wasn't going to stop us from going forward. We knew we brought two different lifestyles to the table, but we discovered that our love and experiences would bring a powerful spirit to the relationship that was unfolding. Somehow we knew with God at the center we could overcome the challenges that arose.

CHAPTER THIRTEEN:

Learning to Play Whack-A-Mole with my Unhealthy Voice

Addicts and trauma survivors are not the only ones who when faced with triggers want to run from the challenge. It is our basic human response to have the "fight or flight reaction" and it's controlled by the hypothalamus. It was first recognized by Walter Cannon in 1929. "It is a sequence of internal processes that prepares the aroused organism for struggle or escape. It's triggered when we interpret a situation as threatening. The resulting response depends on how the organism has learned to deal with threat, as well as an innate fight or flight 'program' built into the brain."[10] Addicts have a little bit more of an extreme response but it's okay if you have it. You are human. This will help you to be compassionate with yourself as you approach these. Also, given the societal obsession with weight, don't think you are alone in this journey. You are most certainly not! That's why I wrote this section of the book and went through it myself, so that I could pave the way for you to walk. Whatever you do, resist your desire to fix!

Triggers are internal and external. We wish we could know everything about every one and when they were coming, but then life would be completely boring, wouldn't it? There are many scientific terms for how they arrive but I've noticed they come on fast with things like emotions, thoughts, visual stimuli, or physical cravings. It's all about how I'm reacting. If I'm in recovery, I'm that much more constant and grounded in the face of them. They will most certainly come, but knowing they will arise and knowing I don't have to act like they aren't there helps me to accept that they are and I can get through them with the tools I've been given. This trigger awareness process especially at the beginning was one of the hardest things in my recovery process but it was also the best getting to know myself and things I could have done. I hope you enjoy what you find out in yourself.

My Unhealthy Voice Triggers

I needed my meetings to stay away from the alcohol because in a college environment, the ease of ability to use it as a stress reliever is just too easy. The food itself was much tougher, obviously. We can't cut that out of our lives. My Food Triggers showed up everywhere. If I could see it, smell it or remember it, I could be triggered by it. The biggest triggers were obviously sugar and bread. Thankfully my food plan kept me on track. It also helped me notice what my Unhealthy Voices would have loved to have! Anytime things got tough, it would try to make me fantasize of baked goods or chocolate covered anything. While classmates would devour home baked cookies I would eat my home cooked meals and stay grounded. I noticed things I now affectionately call "endless" snacks, which were bags of anything from chips to pretzels. If there wasn't an end to it, I could find no end to it. The funny thing is I wasn't even a salt lover! As I started to notice these, I really recognize the whole concept of "moderation." The definition of it is supremely different for each of us and it's something I love to help people break down to find their own personal Healthy Voice with it.

If you can believe it, healthy foods triggered me. I could take any "healthy" food and make it unhealthy. It did not matter if it said organic or low-sugar or if it was a 100-calorie pack. Someone could tell me they were gluten-free or something "looked" healthy and I should eat that and it wouldn't make a difference. All the food rules from someone else were just that, someone else's truth. If it tasted good the label did not matter I don't care how pretty it looked. I could do damage and feel shame about it. Not only that, I could be triggered in the sense I learned about in treatment—both mentally and physically. Things that people called "healthy" could make me get an intense rush of hunger and the Unhealthy Voice. Other things that were fine for one person just weren't for me because they didn't feel good to my body when I ate them. It was another sign that I truly had to find my own way in this maze of food recovery.

Let me give you an example. Often times the "healthiest" foods gave my IBS the biggest flare-ups. I absolutely love Quinoia but my stomach doesn't. I would get so bloated that my Unhealthy Voice would bark for days and tell me I was fat. It would physically hurt to walk. I'd be bending over in pain to the point that I had to talk to my nutritionist about an alternative. Just because it was healthy didn't mean it was working for my body. The same thing goes with giving power to healthy labels. By the time I was navigating triggers, I knew how sensitive I had to be to these. The biggest example of this was pasta. It didn't matter if it was white or wheat pasta triggered a massive sugar rush in my body. I could not touch it. Many times it caused cramping and I can remember all the races I was stuck in the port-o-john because of it. Not only that, it made me hungrier. It never, ever filled me up. It may make no sense to you, but when I'd eat it, I'd be hungry for hours, sometimes days. It wouldn't matter how much of it I had. I thought I was crazy, but that's how my body was reacting. When I made the connection, the light went off and I knew pasta was a killer substance for me. I know I'm not the only one.

When I was walking my recovery and navigating my triggers I met a woman named Denise. She'd had gastric bypass surgery before and lost a lot of weight with it. Whenever she'd hear me talk about my food addiction, she'd identify completely with it. She also identified with the alcohol part of it. After her surgery, the alcohol became a problem. At one point she found herself in the hospital almost bleeding to death from having a few one night. We started to talk about the root of her food addiction and the alcohol with it. She spoke about how she wished she'd heard this before she had the surgery so she could have been better equipped to navigate the post-operation. It made me grateful that I took the path I did, and that I could be there for her to share my experience. Finally I asked her, "What was it that you picked up first?" I knew it wasn't the alcohol. She walked me into the kitchen and said, "It was this box of pasta." I looked at her and said, "For us that might as well be the drink. It's the gateway." She realized in that moment how one harmless box of pasta had triggered such an awful experience. It showed me a more powerful example than ever of how much the food and the alcohol went together for people like the both of us. It's up to each of us to make the choice not to go there, to know ourselves enough that certain things trigger us as individuals and we have a choice to make as we walk.

Trigger Places were another thing for me to navigate. Obviously, the grocery store was a big Trigger Place since it's where I used to go get my fix and bring it home to isolate, but other places were too. The bakery case at Starbucks was a big trigger from my old White House days. The idea of it was just so tempting, not tempting enough though. I knew that it wouldn't fill me up and only make me feel bad about my self. Restaurants were another one. From walking in the door, to choosing from the huge menu, to staying present during the meal—it's a process of continuous turning it over to your Higher Power. Chip baskets at Mexican places, bread before your meal, and bread with everything! It was not easy to navigate! I will never forget going to my old collegiate late night hangout, Nick's with my recovery friends. It was a total blind-side trigger. It brought me back to who I was when I was drinking and eating, but I was okay. I got through it. I keep getting through every restaurant experience and getting stronger each time by making the best possible healthy choice I can! I don't always get it right but that is okay! From each experience I can learn. I can go to places where I've made the wrong choice in the past and make a different choice based on what I learned. For example, a local restaurant has a balsamic dressing that is just too good. It's one of those things you think "healthy." Well, one day I realized how Unhealthy Voice it was for me. I was immediately starving. I finished my meal and thankfully didn't freak out but knew I had to get home and get protein in my body that would make my body get back to normal. In the past, I would have easily gone home and eaten everything. Not this time. Another trigger place is a place that we all love, called Whole Foods. I used to go there and go to town down those aisles. I'd literally spend my "whole paycheck" as they say. I was in overdrive buying everything just because I wanted it. Now I go to have a nice healthy meal and get what I need, not everything I see that I want. What used to be a trigger place has become a Healthy Voice place for me. What a blessing! I have had to limit a lot of my restaurant choices, which isn't necessarily a bad thing because I just don't love a lot of what's out there that isn't home made. Pizza places are a place I just have to avoid but I like my home made Ezekial pizzas better anyway.

Specific Sensory Triggers can catch you by surprise. Now I can observe how powerful a smell is and not choose instead of going, "I have to have that!" The perfect example is Krispy Kreme. I get out of the car at Office Depot to buy supplies, and I can smell the fresh donuts. I often say out loud, "Crack!" My sense of smell for places like that, Panera's bakery and Subway—really anything with bread is highly sensitive. When you walk in the Notre Dame Bookstore coffee shop, often times the big pretzels or their famous Notre Dame chocolate chip cookies are baking. I can avoid going into many of these place. I can't pretend that I always can or I'd be living in a hole, but I can make a different choice if I enter them.

Trigger Times are a big one as well. I had been numbing myself through these times for 30 years so there were going to be times of the day, week, month and year that I would be triggered. Now, I had to face the music. I had to confront stressful days and my most vulnerable time of the day, nighttime. That is when I would normally isolate and binge. I was grateful when I had other things to do at night, including being with people. The holidays were really tough, as they are for so many people. They have always been tough for me. Now, my relationships with my family were changing and I was also around more easily accessible food. Now, that is a trigger environment. I think we do not give these events enough credit. Instead, we sugar binge our way through them. It was tough going through each "sugar" holiday and not getting the 10 different types of chocolate Mom would normally send. I missed the sugar fix and I missed the love I felt from those care packages Mom sent. I had to separate Mom's love from the chocolate. The first holidays in recovery can be sketchy as you are finding your way. I stayed in South Bend for the first Thanksgiving and decided to go home at Christmas. I visited both Mom and Dad out East. Little did I know that I was so fresh in recovery, I was not quite ready to jump into time with the family. I had not quite figured out my way yet. Some people do not have as much trouble with this. I think for some reason I thought I could handle it more smoothly. Thankfully, God got me through it. Prior to my treatment, there is no way I would have gotten through it without using one of my drugs. Instead I walked through it with my Higher Power and my tools of recovery.

As if that was not enough, there were also Behavior/Escape Triggers. We all have our own ways of escaping. I know mine. You probably know yours. The key is in recognizing them. Knowing what you want to use as your escape and what makes you want to escape will help you know yourself. I know that the minute I can call our something that is making me want to escape, I feel more at peace. Sometimes it takes longer than others, but it always helps. In the moment I can say, "What's going on that makes me want to run mentally, emotionally, environmentally, physically, this week, this month, right now?" I can also say, "How is it making me feel?" I can also say, "What is it making me want to do?" Bingo! I realize what's going on and I realize how much pressure I'm putting on myself and I'm better. It's just my Unhealthy Voice wants me to run and I don't have to follow suit. Just because someone in the rooms of alcohol recovery wants to plow through a dozen donuts, doesn't mean that I can too. Knowing this can save me a lot of trouble. I remember one time a friend ate a donut very slowly. I was amazed as she put it down after each bite. I just looked at her, leaned over and said, "You are so not a food addict. I would have been thinking about my third donut by my first bite of that." Because I knew my other trigger, I could call it out and even laugh about it.

The "Thin Ideal" Trigger is everywhere. It's so overloaded that it needs it's own trigger section. If this triggers you, you have to know you are not alone. You also have to know that you can drop the belief that you need to get there. All it does is drive us further into the belief that we aren't good enough until we get the perfect body. This is so why we need to find our own Healthy Voice for Life because thin is not the ideal life anymore. We are more than our bodies and if thin is where we get, then great. We have to live from within my friends. If we don't, we'll forever be chasing this ideal. So whenever you see it, acknowledge it and keep walking. For me that meant being very conscious when reading magazines to the point that I didn't have much to read except a few articles. I had to delete the spamming thin idea emails from my inbox and not turn to the social media obsession with the thin ideal. I had to keep focusing on the goal that thin is not my goal. If someone says to me, "You look skinny!" I get triggered simply because it's not my ideal in life anymore. I'm all about redefining that.

The "Healthy Ideal" Trigger is another reason I created this Healthy Voice. I officially grant you permission to define your own healthy through your Healthy Voice! You are more than just the physical! Stop making yourself nuts listening to your best friend tell you what is healthy because what is healthy for her may not be for you! If you've learned anything from my crazy journey, I hope it's to find your own Healthy Voice and stop looking to everyone else to define it for you. It almost makes me crazy when people say, "Oh you are so healthy." Really? Because I'd love to hear what your definition of that is. It's just as relative as skinny and fat! Healthy is a balance for each of us. Where marathons and cleanses are a boundary for me, they may be your sweet spot. We all have our own sweet spots and it's up to us to find it. More importantly, it's up to us not to compare it to someone else's or try to compete! If we just keep staying true to our self, we'll keep staying on course.

Can you tell I'm passionate about people finding their own definition of healthy with their Healthy Voice?

Media Triggers. This is where all of that, "You aren't thin enough, healthy enough, pretty enough or good enough" plays out. It's all about how we respond to it. If you want to center your life around the rest of the world's idea of thin or healthy, then that's great but if you want to be grounded in your Healthy Voice when you experience it—you've got to be ready because they aren't going to stop telling you that you need to fix yourself. At least, I haven't seen them stop yet. Here's what I've found. From the alcohol and food commercials to the dieting ads at every turn, you really can't get away from it. Then you've got television shows getting people to lose weight at mach speed and reality shows of people with perfect bodies. Or you've got movie stars looking glamorous making you think you've got to look that way. If you really sit back and watch like I did during this time, and still do—you'd be amazed at the amount of triggers you'd see and how everyone just wants to fix and not let anyone just find their own Healthy Voice.

I got a small sneak peak into the window of this world when a Biggest Loser Contestant named Courtney Crozier came to Memorial Health and Lifestyle to speak. I was curious to find out if she'd found her Healthy Voice. I was pleasantly surprised to her how much of a Healthy Voice she had in her heart. Whether she was on the show or not, her sharing her story gave people a lot of hope. She spoke of how they rejected her a handful of times to be a contestant and so she lost 120 pounds before she even got on the show then 110 when she got on. She said something about how losing it before made her realize it wasn't television she needed, but confidence in herself. That's the kind of Healthy Voice I like to hear. She took her physical transformation and became a Healthy Voice Role Model.

CHAPTER 14:

Learning and Growing in Year Two

As I continued to work my recovery program one day at a time I kept turning deeper into my Higher Power for strength. Life seemed to get tougher, but more worth it because it became so much more fulfilling to know myself even more. Each day I was turning more to the tools that gave me life and less to the life of isolation where I had cornered myself.

Everyday Life

At this point I was continuing my graduate degree and training to be a Life Coach. At the same time I was questioning whether or not I had it in me, "Do I have what it takes? Can I do work I'm passionate about and be happy? Can I make money for myself?" I couldn't believe I was pondering this at my age but it was okay. I am so grateful for the women in my coaching tribe who championed me. They showed me I could do it. At every step, I was battling that voice of fear telling me I could not. Yet I did.

Because I was so passionate about health, I tagged myself as a wellness coach and found that most people wanted help losing the weight, getting the right foods or workout. That's understandable, but I wanted to go deeper. I found that because of the innate Unhealthy Voice ingrained in us by society, it was going to be hard to take people there. So I decided to be the Healthy Voice. I decided to write this book and speak as much as I could about the need for the Healthy Voice in this country. I spoke about all the things that distract us in society, in our communities, in industry, and in our own homes. I found that the women who were yearning for something greater were the ones getting ready to grow up—college kids. I taught camps to summer kids in elementary school who soaked it up and felt the love of the Healthy Voice. I stayed in touch with the Food Addiction Professionals group, many of whom are doing amazing things for food addicts but aren't being heard on so many levels. It's like there is this big connect—people with all of this substantial knowledge that are speaking to the choir and people of all ages that want the information but can't get it. I thought, there had to be a way I could connect the two with my voice. At the same time I'm working in a running shop listening to people who are inspired to get into running, talking about the Healthy Voice.

Financial Responsibility

At the same time I'm trying to listen to my own Healthy Voice in the place of finances. For a long time it was just as much of an Unhealthy Voice as the food and alcohol. My Unhealthy Voice had always told me I could never be responsible with my own financial matters. Starting a business and managing my own finances were two things I wanted to be smart about in my life. So I decided to address it and reverse that irresponsible voice to a responsible one by taking Dave Ramsey's Financial Peace University. His program complemented every other part of my journey. Credit cards couldn't be part of the equation for me anymore. I'd spent carelessly, and I wanted to "live like no one else so I could live like no one else." Having all the material things in the world just didn't mean anything to me anymore. I'd been given so much by my parents growing up and I was grateful, but life was so much simpler now. If God wanted me to have those things, I could trust that He would bring them in His time, not mine. It certainly wouldn't mean I wouldn't want them because I'm human but this program and getting accountable would help me to stay balanced and tuned into my Healthy Voice with it.

Navigating Through Food Fears

My relationship with food was getting so much better. Food was truly becoming more physical than emotional fuel. What did start to stress me out though was the rigidity. When I was in treatment I learned a lesson about my perfectionism. I literally never though I had it because, "I'm not perfect so I can't be a perfectionist." It was hurting me because I couldn't just be me, ever. I was never good enough in anything. So when my perfectionism resurfaced with the food, I didn't like it. I was afraid of being too perfect and afraid of not doing it perfectly enough. I had to relax. I noticed it was my Unhealthy Voice trying to cling to food as the control and center of my life. I was done with perfect. I was working a program of progress not perfection. I'd found a God who was in charge not me. I had kids around me every day. I was sometimes in situations where I'd have to adapt with food. The world just didn't revolve around me and that was a good thing! It was these times where I found the deepest surrender with God. I found it fitting that He asked me to into that deeper place with Him by way of the thing I never wanted to let go. He would say, "It's okay, I will carry you through this." So in those situations where my fear came up around food, I trusted Him. If I freaked out too much, I knew it was the devil of my Unhealthy Voice. I needed to keep turning to Him. Making food more powerful than God wasn't working for me, but the Food Plan and the other tools sure were. I did have moments where I tested Him—as we all do in life. Personally, I had to challenge those old Unhealthy Voice beliefs that foods from my past had some sort of power over me. Think of Girl Scout Cookie and Dunkin Donuts munchkins. I had to taste these to take their power away and found they had none. That was more freeing for me than avoiding them. By facing my fear and tasting one, I found I didn't need them. It was just little Meredith who loved the taste as a kid and probably the emotional freedom. Today, they don't have that power. I can choose my Healthy Voice instead and that is in itself empowering.

Navigating People

The beauty of finding more relationships in our life is that life begins to get fuller. The thing about relationships is they aren't easy. They have their bumpy roads and high points. The joy is in staying on the road, being there for each other when you fall, and letting each other walk on your own two feet. The problem is that we have this ideal in society that isn't exactly a Healthy Voice for any of us. Shows like The Bachelor, romantic comedies, and family sitcoms make us think that our life needs to be just like television. Yet our relationships are real life and unique to us. Where we falter is when we let relationships throw us completely off track from the core of our Healthy Voice.

Some relationship triggers are just People Triggers. They can be people we see every week or every day. They will always trigger us and the choice is up to us in how we react. I am still learning myself! When we interact with people, we forget that we have our own histories and system of triggers totally separate from each other. All you have to do is think of the simple differences between man and woman to recognize this. How long have so many struggled going, "They just don't understand!" The truth is, we weren't meant to! We were meant to complement each other! The same thing goes with the people who trigger us the most. Usually, they are in our lives to teach us something. I've learned they are often our greatest teachers. If I'm triggered, I have to look at what's going on with me, but I have to be very careful not to blame myself. I did this for many years, and can still find my Unhealthy Voice trying to do it. I have to remember that if someone dumps something it is for them to deal with, not me. I don't have to blame myself or try to fix them. I can own my part and let them own theirs. God's got us both figured out. This is hard stuff to learn! Taking things personally is one thing that I know I do all the time. I often wonder if something is about me, but most of the time it never is so!

Don Miguel Ruiz says it best in his book "The Four Agreements": "Don't take anything personally. Nothing others do is because of you. What others say and do is a projection of their own reality, their own dream. When you are immune to the opinions and actions of others, you won't be the victim of needless suffering."

Other people's expectations and approval can be very difficult to navigate with our Healthy Voice, especially since the journey is all about finding our truest self. We can't let other people's judgments of our choices keep us from our truth. We are learning on the way, how our Healthy Voice is guiding us. We don't need approval from anyone else but the one who created us. There will be people, experts, professionals, and even people we love that will tell us we can be better, healthier and stronger. That is great. There will be others who will say we aren't good enough. There is a good chance we'll interpret some of it as that Unhealthy Voice. It's then that we have to remember no one is the authority on us. God is the only authority on us. We must honor our bodies and respect the advice and counsel of those people who can make us get better. We can't rely on them for our truth or self-worth. They will only take us to one piece of our truth. Their wisdom will guide us to our healthiest self but it's just one channel. Only we can find and know our whole Healthy Voice truth.

Other people and the rest of the world may have expectations of us, but we're getting there. I've found my highest expectations are the ones I put on myself. The truth is that this whole expectations business has gotten out of control. We put too much on ourselves, on the people we love and on the world. We have to realize we aren't perfect. We have to stop expecting to reach every goal and dream in superhuman capacity and just enjoy the journey! Goals and dreams being reached are much better than expecting ourselves to reach our unrealistic expectations. They only bring disappointments. Leave your outcomes to God and just keep walking. Remember, you are the one that is living this life. You have got your Higher Power with you all the way. So trust it. It's not always easy, but He is good.

Trigger Conversations and Situations are going to happen. They will happen with these people in your life and people you just happen to meet. They will trigger you and you've just got to walk through them. Some will be harder than others, especially if they are emotionally charged. Bring God into them and trust that He will carry you. All it takes is a trigger person that leads to a trigger conversation or situation and that is when you can be in your Healthy Voice and reacting. Stay aware of how your Unhealthy Voice gets you in this trap! I try to record when it does, whether I'm able to stop them before they start or it's after the fact. Just like people, these things can teach us something. Sometimes you will have to step away because it's toxic. Other times you have to talk through it. Other times you have to be guided through it. Whatever it is, the difference is now we get to face the dark with the light instead of run from the dark. We can set boundaries with people even if we didn't learn how to do it! That's a whole other book but it's a good topic! Just remember each conversation—someone else is bringing their own truths and stories.

Finding a Healthy Voice Companion for the Journey

All I know is whoever said relationships are supposed to be easy didn't know what they were talking about! For me, the beauty lies in the struggle. That's how you grow stronger together. We walk the hills and the valleys together. Finding your Healthy Voice in a relationship isn't about finding the perfect one that will complete you. It's about finding the one who will walk alongside you. Standing by someone in the thick and thin is tough stuff if you never really learned how to do it. Let me tell you it is worth it! I'd rather run this life with someone who reflects me than keep running until I find someone that could "complete me." I like my complement! I also like the life we are creating together. I like the life we are living alongside each other in the everyday. I used to think that having a man beside me threatened me as a strong, independent woman, maybe because I saw how strong my Mom was. For me it was becoming both. I could be a strong woman and also have this strong man beside me and that was a good thing. He was someone I didn't have to be dependent on. He supported every dream I had and loved me for who I was, not who I was becoming. One of the biggest blessings has been the time I've spent with his three children. We've had fun together and we've had our struggles, but that's the beauty. We just keep walking together. I get to witness them growing up and it's like a mirror of my younger self. These kids teach me so much about life. They show me how much the world does not revolve around me and that's a true blessing. I love being around them.

It's funny because each day we walk this, I become more and more passionate about children of divorce and blended families. I see how much strength you can give to children out of struggle rather than pounding them with this Scarlett Letter of being the victim. I can't wait to see what the Lord does with the Healthy Voice and children of divorce or stepfamilies because it's where I believe part of this walk is leading us. No kid deserves to be victimized by the stigma of divorce! All are loved no matter what!

Knowing My One True Healthy Voice

As I was navigating these relationships, the triggers, the recovery journey, all of my weaknesses and strengths on the journey, I was realizing more every day how much I needed Him. I wanted to be in a deeper commitment to Him and our relationship. I started to see how much of my life he was preparing me to be in this place where I'd be ready for this. I couldn't believe that I had a relationship but I could grasp the concept of going deeper into it. So I listened from my heart to what he was saying—through music, through the rooms of recovery, through people, and in church. I kept hearing Him calling me so I could find greater healing.

I was conflicted though because I had these two sides of him—an Unhealthy Voice god and a Healthy Voice one—one who was waiting for me to be good enough and judging me, and the other who never did and loved me unconditionally. I wanted more of that God who loved me unconditionally that I was coming to know. I was afraid of the Unhealthy Voice god—he would hate me, ridicule me, and judge me. I just kept walking away from the fear and towards the love. I knew Mike had gone to some church that was different from mine that he said spoke to him. So one day I decided to go to Granger Community Church. I fell in love with it the minute I walked into it. The love, joy and peace surrounding you the minute you walk in the door was overwhelming. I wanted what these people had. I found a community where people were showing up with a smile on their face and being authentic. They know they aren't perfect but they wanted to be better people for God. Then I heard the music that I'd been waking up to every morning since I was in Washington and cried.

I heard the Pastors get up every week and talk about walking with Jesus. It was right there with my walk in recovery. They would interpret the Bible and share about their own struggles and weaknesses, even their times of questioning God. I kept hearing these messages from the Pastors who would get up there and make you feel almost every week like the message was made just for you. They would share about relevant messages of everyday life. This sharing made me feel like God was meeting me in my everyday life. It was powerful. You could actually talk to the Pastors after the service and say thank you or pray with them. It was just another amazing part that showed me nothing came between God and I. Thinking he was "up there, not down here" was just not the case anymore. This place was showing me that and I was immensely grateful. You could tell why God had chosen them to lead the people of this church to Christ.

Everything just started to make sense. I still went back to my old church for a while, but I found that the Lord kept calling me in love to this place. So I just let in the light and love. I let go of the fear and judgment and focused on Him because this was between the two of us. I started to transform on a deeper spiritual level than I ever imagined. He was healing me like He said he would. Not only that, He was showing me that He understood my pain. I didn't have to be good enough for him, or perfect enough, or even feel guilty about the fact that he died on the cross. I got to completely change the way I viewed Him through what I learned about Him as a man. Christmas is about how he came down to earth to show me that whatever I'd been through, he'd been through it too and I could find comfort in that. He died not for me to feel guilty, but so that I could give my sins to Him to carry, for with Him my burden is light! He is why I got into recovery. He is why I'm here on this earth.

That's when I realized in the fall of 2009—that if He is why I'm here, then I want to show Him I'm committed to His purpose and His plan. So I made the commitment to get baptized. I'd done it as a kid but for me this was about meeting myself where I was at that moment, and really meeting God where He was meeting me. I needed Him to keep walking and I wanted Him to know that in the most symbolic way I could. So it happened and it was one of the happiest days of my life. One of the songs that played leading up to it as well as in the video when they replayed it at church was a song called "Healing Begins" by the band Tenth Avenue North. It's powerful. I hope that you'll go check out the lyrics because of the way the song starts out and how every time you are in that spot it just meets you wherever you are—is a beautiful thing.

CHAPTER FIFTEEN:

Going About Life in Year Three

By year three, I felt like I was starting to get the hang of this new life. I realized that there would be triggers and bad days but if I just kept walking and trusting God, he'd take care of what I couldn't do myself. I started to feel less like a weed and more like a flower budding. The gifts started to show up in my career path, where I was able to give back with the Healthy Voice to the world. I could finally start seeing why he'd taken me down this road. Of course, the triggers still were hairy. There was always something I could learn if I just remained surrendered and willing.

How I saw God Was Starting to Lead Me to His Purpose

In doing the work I was doing in my own life and in my work, God was beginning to show me what He had planned. Program directors came to me that were helping people find healthy lifestyles but realizing that behavior modification was the sweet spot. Women that wanted a healthy life but a way to navigate better behaviors. Women that wanted something deeper, more spiritual than behaviors. Fitness-minded women who wanted this Healthy Voice for the women they lead. A CEO that wanted something for his audience that was more than your typical relapse model and a hospital that realized obesity was about disease management, not the fix. On top of it all, the college women still wanted to find their way through the maze with their Healthy Voice. It's like He had this connect the dots and I was just supposed to follow Him and draw them so He could show me where to go.

First it was the American Heart Association Better U Program in South Bend, Indiana. I was the behavior modification coach and taught my first group of women on a fitness journey how to find their Healthy Voice and avoid all the distractions while they take this weight loss journey. That experience showed me how truly powerful this can be. I coached one woman named Kelly Hohl who had gone through the program. She was having a rough week and as many of us do, giving more power to the scale than necessary. So she bravely got one-on-one coached by me and by the end of it we realized the scale was the culprit. She was angry it wasn't giving her the results she wanted. Who can relate to that? I'd hit my sweet spot because in that moment she realized that the scale did not have to have all that power and it certainly did not have to own her self-worth. Did it make her get perfect? Absolutely not . . . but the revelation did change her mind about the scale and that is power. Later she sent me a message:

"I have discovered after working with you that I use a lot of things to punish myself for either the bad choices I've made or for not being strong or brave enough to make the changes that I think will help confront my Unhealthy Voice. I have found that since I have met you and listened to you that I am starting to feel much more comfortable in my own skin. I don't hardly ever step on the scale anymore and if I do it's strictly as a point of reference—more to see if I need to make any changes in my life than to find out how much I weigh and how bad I'll feel about myself. I really should get a tattoo that says, "The scale is not your worth." Meredith, that

comment was the beginning of a turnaround for me . . . I don't know if I can ever thank you enough."

What she did not know is she did the work herself. I was only there to witness her Healthy Voice coming into power. Another woman in that same program would lose over 100 pounds and we'd meet again on the journey. I found out later how she realized she had a Healthy Voice.

Then, I went to Cleveland Clinic and learned all about everything they are doing to help people get past their weight struggles, from coaching to well-rounded programs of fitness and nutrition to an obesity summit. After leaving the Clinic I got a call from my Uncle telling me about a project with a CEO that was interested in behavior modification and the disease management approach to obesity for their clients. I remember calling my Dad so excited about the prospect of the project but also the impact I could make with the message of the Healthy Voice all because God brought me on this journey. So I just kept walking forward.

I was hired as a consultant to the Cleveland Clinic to work on this Behavior Modification and Motivation curriculum alongside Dr. Paul Terpeluk, DO and my uncle and Gary Heavin, the CEO of Curves International. I couldn't believe that there was a man leading so many women to healthier lifestyles who got it. Gary made the connection that the relapse model wasn't the ticket and he wanted to help women find a healthy lifestyle. I was up to the task. With God by my side, every step of the journey felt almost surreal. I felt humbled, honored and blessed to be this channel for all of these women. I felt grateful to be coming alongside these accomplished people, but it felt right—like we'd all done what we'd done to come to this place. All of the struggle I had when I was in government, hoping that someone would hear my voice for those who needed it—now the right people weren't just hearing it, they were taking it all in and using it to reach the people who needed it! I was moved by the entire experience at every level. I'm still humbled. I'm grateful for the reach and amazed at the impact it's still having because a few people came together.

During this whole time I'm still having college girls reach out to me. One in particular I'd met about a year before was coming to mind. I knew she'd just graduated from St. Mary's College in South Bend, Indiana and she was starting to tune into her Healthy Voice. I also knew she needed a summer job before she started grad school. Her name is Tavierney Rogan and I will never forget calling her up with the opportunity of a lifetime in helping me with this project. In the process of editing the scripts and the teachings, she learned how to find her own Healthy Voice. I couldn't be more proud of her journey and who she's becoming in finding her Healthy Voice. It was an amazing experience to have representation from the generation I'm trying to reach help me with the generation that needs this Healthy Voice so much.

As we wrapped the project up in the spring of 2010, I decided to go on a retreat out to Sedona, Arizona with a group of Martha Beck Coaches. It was exactly what I needed to tune back into my Healthy Voice at the time. Boy did I get it (but of course Sedona is one of those places where you can't help but get the vortexes aligning with you). These women came alongside me like they did when I first started the journey and helped me realize my full potential again. They helped me see what I love and how I'm going to lead and the women I'm going to lead. Their light reflected my light back to me. We took a silent hike together up Enchantment Resort (imagine 25 strong women not talking as they walk!). I heard God talking to me again as I picked up a Red Rock that fit my fist perfectly. He told me to trust in Him and keep letting go of Mom, letting her be herself, and letting me be myself. He showed me one woman who had addiction in her family that related to this Healthy Voice and wanted to read the book. He showed me another woman named Lynn, who lived in my hometown and understood what I was trying to do. He showed me another woman who was a tremendous Healthy Voice for me the whole weekend and didn't even know it! Michelle Rashid—you are one Healthy Voice chic. Back home in Seattle, Washington she motivates women to spin and run in a group called "Fit

B**%#". I can't wait to visit them and for a run! We went on a run and she just kept lifting me up in spirit, telling me how great this work is going to be, but not even realizing how powerful she was for me! Then, it's our last morning there. I get a call from my dad randomly at 7 in the morning coming back from a run. It was one of those "I just called to tell you I love you" calls. He shared how proud he was and he knew could not have asked for a better daughter. It was as if I was not going to talk to him again. I saw it as God's way of planting that voice in my mind so I would never forget how much he did love me and support me. How lucky I was, so lucky that I shed tears of joy as I stood in one of my most favorite beautiful places. It was like I brought the energy to me.

New Trigger: Travel and Reentry

Of course the Unhealthy Voice is going to pop up, especially when things are going good! Traveling is where it showed up. This is where I was grateful to have a Food Plan and the ability to prepare my meals. But I also knew the triggers were everywhere while I was en route and on the actual trip. It didn't matter whether it was business or personal. They would just be there. My role was to trust God to carry me through them and stay as grounded as possible in my Food Plan and tools. This was a Healthy Voice journey unto itself. Someday I want to write a guide just for traveling with your Healthy Voice. Airports, rest stops, and really anything in transit seem to be the breeding grown for the Unhealthy Voice going haywire. The same thing goes for when you get to your destination. In transit, it's like, "I need this food to keep me going" or "I can eat cinnamon buns and nobody will see!" Then you get there and it's like all hell breaks loose.

So what I did was pack my lunch for every trip, ask for a fridge in my room if they didn't have one, hit a convenience store for the basics and be on my way. If that weren't possible, I'd look for a breakfast with protein and fruit. I found it fascinating to be at some conferences that were focused on healthy lifestyles or eating disorders and the sugar or lack of healthy choices were everywhere. People have their gluten allergies, but my idea of an afternoon snack is not a brownie. My idea of breakfast is not something bread. It's protein no matter what because I can't start my day with a blood sugar freight train. If it was a personal trip, driving I'd pack a cooler for all possible snacks and meals. I still do. Vacations, I obviously can't bring my whole meals for the week but I adapt when I get there. Mike and I went to Victoria Canada, which was pretty easy to navigate for food. We also went to Costa Rica. My Unhealthy Voice really wanted to sabotage me and tell me I was not going to be able to handle it. Not true. It was great. I was so proud of myself. The food was fresh and fabulous. Not only that, I didn't have to freak out about not working out like I would have in the past and just enjoy the present!

Preparing and reentering after a trip is a whole other ball of wax. We all have this Unhealthy Voice. I know I used to, and it can be about any event we are planning, not just trips. It says the weeks we are preparing to go, "Starve yourself so you can look good when you get there." I know many college girls that do this before going home for the holidays so they can look thin for their parents. Then it says when we're returning, "It's time to go on a diet! You've been bad!" Hello Unhealthy Voice. It is wrong. When I'm getting ready to travel, I try to stick to my Healthy Voice that tells me to tune into my Food and Fitness Truth. That same voice is with me on the trip to make the best choices I can and even when I return to help me acclimate to being home. Sometimes we need a little time and space to adapt in both ways, but we certainly do not need to beat ourselves up about our weight. Traveling has taught me a huge lesson. No matter what, God has my back. He is always going to take care of me. If I do my part and take care of myself in the best way I can, he will take care of the rest.

Old Triggers: Fitness and Working Out Balance

That brings me to the good old fitness and workout triggers. When we are getting ready to go on a trip, trying to reach a goal for an event or just dealing with stress, we can freak out about not getting our workouts. Just like anything else, these are exactly the times when we can trust that God knows better than our stupid Unhealthy Voice. Working out is great for our health and our stress levels, but we don't need it to fix us. We are okay! We have to give ourselves time to find our own fitness truths. Believe me, there's nothing like learning this when you are a runner and all you've got is your own two feet and some sneakers. If you are a runner you understand.

I'd have to watch myself no matter what. If Mike and I were running together and he wanted to kick it into high gear, I had to voice my Healthy Voice and set the boundary that it triggered my Unhealthy Voice of fixing. I also had to learn to recognize the voice that tells me when I'm running that I can't do it, or it's too hard. That's just not the right voice to listen to because it's telling me to give up. I don't need that. I can listen for the gentle voice that says rest though. I have to call my Healthy Voice into every run, and run from my spirit, not from my physical self. I do shorter races like 10ks and 5ks and Half-Marathons. I do other activities like yoga and cycling. As long as I know that running is not my only thing, there is always something I can do to keep from getting triggered. Running was just for fun and only one of the activities I do. I didn't have to compete in races with my best friend who could outrun me by a mile. She's just got the speed and I'm proud of her for that! I don't have to beat myself up if I have a bad race day. I could be with myself on the journey with every step. More importantly, I don't have to take that Unhealthy Voice with me on the run. Now, I can be very conscious of that self-defeating voice. It is still important to talk about it though because it's not talked about enough. I believe, it's through sharing that defeating voice that we can get beyond it!

CHAPTER SIXTEEN:

The Event That Changed my Life in Year Three

I had no idea what God had planned. It's a good thing I didn't, because I wouldn't have wanted to know from a tarot reading what was next. I had to let God prepare me for the biggest storm of my life in His way. Through chance moments he would do just that. He would heal one of the most important relationships in my life. I am truly grateful that I could be present for each moment and look back at them as memories now because they are truly powerful memories for me. I am grateful I wasn't sick during any of them because I wouldn't have recognized them as gifts. I can now see how God works everything together for good if we just trust Him. I'm learning from His love, that it's not by controlling love that we find it. It's by being it that we shine it out. It's by letting everybody be who they are and learning to be whom we are that things happen. Then we can come alongside each other when the storms hit. That's what makes life truly beautiful.

The Gifts Before the Storm

There were chance events that I had with Dad leading up to that last month of August 2012. There were conversations that were almost heavenly, filled with gratitude for the journey and love of life. I can look back and just see how the Holy Spirit was paving the way for Him, and for us to enter the next phase of a relationship. We didn't know it yet, but each of those chance moments that God had lined up were preparing for a shift—from one of physical to spiritual presence.

There was the time he came to see me speak at the first Binge Eating Disorder Association Conference in Baltimore. We got to have coffee and talk about my book and the Healthy Voice concept, visionary to visionary. He was so excited he was jumping out of his seat. He got to come up to the grand ballroom and watch me share my story and speak of the Healthy Voice light in each leader there. I can still see him sitting there with the biggest smile you can imagine. He was so proud. I will carry it with me every time I speak in front of a crowd for strength. What a gift.

There was the time last November when we got to meet up for the Bush—Cheney Alumni Association Reunion at the Bush Library Groundbreaking in Dallas, Texas. What an experience. I was totally myself and proud of the woman I was becoming. I was proud of him for everything he'd done as Ambassador. It was just very cool to come alongside each other years after we'd left the administration. I'd had an Unhealthy Voice around it all for a long time, even resented the experience, but it had healed over time. This trip had transformed that healing and made it a complete overwhelming sense of gratitude. There we stood at the beginning of the groundbreaking event. The video starts playing with pictures. The music in the background is the Rudy Soundtrack. We just looked at each other, chocked up and said, "Grand Mom." Heaven sent healing on that trip. That's how God works when you show up for His plan.

Then August 2012 came. Dad told me he was going to be down in Austin for a Perry event and it was the night I'd get there. I was excited I would get to see him. Of course, Dad had left me 5 messages telling me I needed to get to the Four Seasons fast so we could get to the event.

Originally I hadn't even planned on going, and actually I was amazed and was excited to go with him! Boy had I changed over the years! Upon arrival, Dad showed up with his best, as always, powerful presence. The man was a genius at his work. I sat and watched with gratitude for having this guy as an example of leadership and passion for your work on my life. Not only that—he was my Dad! This was his night, and I was happy to sit back and watch him shine. Towards the end of the presentation, one of Dad's friends from Texas got up to say, "None of us would be here if it weren't for Ambassador Terpeluk." I looked over and there was Dad, standing to the side of the room in typical Terpeluk fashion. He had his arms crossed over his power suit and tie, cufflinks shining across the front, hair slicked back, smile beaming, and blue eyes shining. What a moment and I got to be there for it. I started to choke up. How accomplished he really was. I was so proud. I also felt extremely lucky to have his genes!

That same night I noticed something else I was grateful for and it came to him like second nature. As a political player and Diplomat, Dad always made the Healthy Choice and chose not to drink at any of these events. He never knew how much of an impact that example had on me. As I watched the other men knock back many drinks, as is the custom in politics, he never did once. Dad did not drink, even as an Ambassador, when people came to the Embassy and brought tons of champagne and wine as gifts! That night, when our meals came to the table, he and I saw the red meat. We knew what it would do to our stomachs and asked for chicken and vegetables. Many politicos don't even think about not diving into a steak to go with the third drink and Dad just didn't even think about it. My Dad was my Healthy Voice on a level he didn't even know. Later that night I was able to thank him for not choosing to drink. He led by example and it gave me that much more courage to be the businesswoman I wanted to be so I was grateful. He laughed at me when I said it, "Duh Meredith, I don't drink!" I'm glad we could laugh about it at the time, but I also know how heavy it was in both our lives. By being the light for me in many ways he was changing his family tree and that was pretty awesome.

Dad left early the next morning. I would see him a week later when Mike and I would make the trip out to Nantucket. My next stop before our trip was visiting Gary and Diane Heavin to talk about my book. They are an incredible couple and I'm truly grateful to have their peace in my life. They said, "Meredith, people need your story. Get the book written!" After leaving their Hill country house I had a quiet, early morning drive to the airport in Austin. I heard God just telling me, "Meredith, would you just get the book done and I'll take care of the rest?" Then I got on the plane and God brought me the Healthy Voice I needed to meet to give me the courage to write it. Her name was Josephine Mays and she was dying for her own Healthy Voice. I guess God just had a plan that wasn't ours. Together we talked about her struggles with her weight and the things that have stopped her from really getting healthy. Through sharing our stories and struggles we got a strong Healthy Voice going together on that long plane ride. I inspired her to really find out more about her Healthy Voice, to even join the gym again. She inspired me to get that book started because she said, "We need it!" We have remained pen pals until this day and she continues to be a source of strength for my own Healthy Voice. I am so glad I met her. She represents so many people who are dying on the inside. People only see the outside and think they know the answer—a weight fix. There is so much more and I'm so glad I got to find out how beautiful she is on the inside and out! I can't wait to meet more people like Josephine and to continue being inspired by her Healthy Voice within.

So here I am, totally inspired to get this book written. One week later, Mike and I were headed to Nantucket. We were going to have to take planes, trains, and automobiles to get there but we didn't care. We wanted to go and they wanted to have us. This trip was one of the most divine gifts I have ever gotten. Even though it had started out with a Perfect Storm Drama Moment, we got there when we got there. I whipped out my can of east coast girl whoop- *&% on the cab driver and the ferry itself that we missed, but none of it mattered. It was all a lesson in patience. God was showing me that everything works together for His good and things don't always go according to my plan. (Shocker). We got the slower ferry, which forced me to chill out. I stood on the bow and watched the sunset with Mike. Then, I called Dad. He said, "Mere, don't worry! It is all good. You are almost here." It calms me down just to think about that conversation; in the grand scheme of things my travel drama meant nothing.

Dad was still there with a big hug at the ferry to pick us up. There he stood in his prepped out clothes, by his Nantucket car, a beat up old white Jeep Grand Cherokee with the wood paneling that always felt like home when he picked me up in it. This would be the best weekend we would ever have. Dad had spent time with Mike and I in South Bend but this was going to be a weekend of just being us. It was an adjustment for my Dad to see me be so serious with a guy. It wasn't about showcasing him as this trophy boyfriend, but just being who we are as a couple around my family. I am beyond grateful for every moment of that weekend. It meant the world to me. It was a Terpeluk family style weekend and my family saw who Mike and I are in real life. It was the best ever. We talked politics, ate dinner out downtown and on the beach at sunset, and laughed so hard sometimes we cried. We had the absolute best charter fishing day of our lives. Dad grilled his best catch that night as we enjoyed more time together. Then, when it came time to leave on Monday, Dad dropped us off down at the harbor for the ferry and handed me a little Notre Dame raincoat for the drizzling rain. I didn't know that would be the last time I would ever see him alive. It would be the last time I would hug him, look into his eyes, see his smile and be able to say, "I love you Dad!" As I was walking away, I could hear him shout it back.

I felt so at peace, from that trip. Life is truly a precious gift not be taken for granted. There are no mistakes. I would call him from Logan airport to tell him how fun the weekend had been and he said the same things. He would also tell me, "Hey, get that book done! It's going to be great." He was so excited for me and about life coming together the way it was. Diane said later, "He was just so happy to see you so happy."

The Day: August 23rd, 2011

One week later, almost to the day, I woke up to a call at 7:22 a.m. from Diane, "I don't know how to tell you this Meredith. Your father is gone." He'd had a heart attack.

The moment I had feared since I was a kid was happening. It was a moment only God could have lifted me up and carried me through. If I hadn't turned my life over to him on May 12, 2008 I couldn't imagine what I'd be doing in this moment. I didn't want to know. I just kept moving through each breath. I hung up the phone with my stepmom and said out loud to heaven, "I have no regrets. Thank you God for healing our relationship." I turned around and fell to my knees saying, "Thank you God for letting us say goodbye in Nantucket. Then I said to Dad, "I love you. I love you. I love you. Thank you for being my Dad." The gratitude I felt was overwhelming. Then, I felt this love wrap around me as if it were the wings of an angel. I could just feel Dad saying, "Everything is going to be all right Mere. I love you." I trusted that.

I stood up and walked in the other room. I looked outside at the tree and I just listened for God's direction. I picked up the phone. I called Mike. I called my sponsor. I called a friend who has always been like a Dad to me. Mike and my sponsor showed up at the front door. I was so grateful to have these people in my life at the absolute toughest moment especially with my family so far away. This pain was gut wrenching but my gratitude for my Dad was beyond beautiful. I couldn't believe how God was blessing me in the moment. God gave me the courage to call Mom, something I was scared to do. We had gone through so many traumas together in the past. I was afraid of her reaction. But she was my Mom and of course she stood like a rock by my side. The Holy Spirit showed up between us. We prayed together. We got on our knees and said the rosary together over the phone. It was truly a moment of grace. It was as if there was no phone or miles between us.

I took calls from family and friends. I got emails and texts, many from people whom I had worked with at the White House and in Austin. These were people who knew my Dad and knew me. It meant so much to share our loss together. At one point I just had to go to take a walk over on Notre Dame's campus like I did countless times with Dad, just to feel his presence. Mike and I drove over on that rainy day. As we approached the woods above the lakes, we found a family a deer. One baby deer stood and watched us like it didn't want to leave. We stood there so long with it, that it felt like Dad saying he wanted to stick around but had to go. For almost 15 minutes we had communion and stillness with that fawn, a moment I will never forget.

We went down to the grotto and gripped hands as we knelt and prayed. We got back home and I went inside. Mike stood on my front porch and said, "Hey, honey. Come out here." I walked outside. The sky was still sprinkling but there was a cloud break with a rainbow. As soon as I walked out the sun was beating right on my face as the rain still fell. It could not have been a bigger sign from Dad. He shouted in that way he would always give you the nudge to show you he loved you. "Hey. Meredith! I know I'm not there right now, but I'm with you in spirit. You know that. I love you so much. Don't you EVER forget that, okay? Have I ever let you down? I'm not going anywhere. Look up here when you can't find me. I'll be your light. I love you Mere." What a dad. He always did tell me he'd always be there for me. Somehow with a spirit like that, I knew that wasn't changing.

"Seeing death as the end of life is like seeing the horizon as the end of the ocean."

—*David Searls*

I woke up the next day and it felt so surreal. I surrounded myself with pictures of him before I went to sleep just to know he was with me, as I still do. He is always with me. We decided to drive out east for the services. I just needed time to process everything, talk to friends, and be with Mike and cry. I could not have gotten on a plane. I got home and I was so glad to see my family, so happy to give Diane and my brother, Trey a hug. He had bracelets made, which I still wear today. They are red, white and blue with Dad's name and the date he went to heaven on the other side. This is something only my Dad's son would do. It is a reminder every minute my Dad is with us. I love that spirit in my brother.

We made it through the next few days a second, a minute, and an emotion at a time. We got through the services. I got to see so many of my Dad's old friends. Some were laughing like Dad was. Others were sad like his spirit was gone. I reminded them his spirit wasn't. "Don't let his light in you go out. Take whatever he taught you and let it shine." That was my plan and I know I'm not the only one he inspired. I'm just one of the lucky two that got to have him as a Dad.

Dad's attitude about life was always very positive. One of the songs at the time was "The Good Life" by One Republic and I would just blast it. Every time I heard it, it would remind me of Dad saying, "Enjoy it Mere!" and his most classic saying, "Isn't this great?" because no matter how bad things are, there is always a bright side. That kind of outlook on life is quite a legacy to leave your kids, your family and everyone you touch.

Gratitude for My Father's Life

We went from a dependent relationship to a "food police" state to seeing each other reach milestones in our lives. He was open to learning and I loved him for it. We cried, we laughed and we grew in our relationship together. If we had not done that footwork, we would have never had the healing we did before he died and our happy memories.

I got to share in the joy of a graduation from Notre Dame sober with my Dad before he died. It was a special gift. I feel like I honored his legacy of love for the school. I get to keep doing it every time I go to a game, go for a run, or spend time with a student. His spirit and energy are all over that place!

We have so many memories back from our political days. There was so much of that White House experience I shared with him. The St. Patrick's Day events, the year we went to the Kennedy Center Honors, and that day of September 11th I'll never forget. I got to see my Dad in all his Ambassadorial glory over in Luxembourg as he showed that country how an American man with a lot of passion for his country, an entrepreneurial spirit, and an ability to bring people together can do great things. Being there for the 50th Anniversary of the Battle of the Bulge, the 4th of July, and the start of the Tour De France with my family are experiences I will cherish. The picture of Dad and Lance up close from the start of the tour is one that will always rest on my desk. I'm so grateful my Dad –our family got to have that experience. Now I can look back and realize that it was maybe another way that God was preparing me for his journey to heaven.

I am so grateful for his light and life because it has shown me that life is change and we get to either embrace it or not. I'm glad he showed me the way to embrace it, especially when my Mom told me that after his father passed when he was young, he took it as an opportunity to keep shining his light. It not only gave me strength to get through it, thinking that if he could get through this, I can. But it gave me strength to commit to the journey and the Healthy Voice.

Navigating the Biggest Feeling Trigger Ever: Grief

I thought when I got to this day that I'd learned to navigate some of my feelings. But I had no idea. Grief is one of the biggest minefields of emotions you can imagine. It felt like I was going through a whole new recovery learning to navigate entirely new triggers all based on missing my Dad. But I was grateful the second time around I was losing him, that I was present. Certainly that was God's plan. It's a whole other book that will come but I wanted to share a few of my early experiences.

I never knew when a huge wave of emotions was going to come, whether it was anger, sadness, or depression. This time instead of walking through a craving, or a trigger with food, I was walking through an experience or a memory. One of the first experiences was going to the Notre Dame Kick-Off Classic football game Labor Day weekend. Because Dad loved ND Football and we had already planned to continue in our family tradition, we went through with it. Thank God we had each other because it was tough for every one of us and laden with reminders of Dad from the bookstore to the football field, but we got through it. It was a first. We knew he was with us, especially when huge storms started to roll in that kept postponing the game. It's like he was trying to change the score himself up there.

Days came and went. Holidays came and went. They weren't easy. I'd be amazed at how my feelings would just stop me in my tracks for a day, or my body would be so tired from missing him that I couldn't move. It took me months in the spring to find out that Fridays were just off days for me. For some reason I missed dad on those days and so I just had to go easy on myself. I was starting to know myself as this new person without him physically present in my life. Some of the absolute hardest times were not being able to call him on the phone during the week to say hi. Other times, I'd call him to get some inspiration because he was always motivating me to believe in myself. Yet, when something good happened and he wasn't there? It broke my heart. It was okay though because missing him made me realize how much I loved him. I was blessed.

I could not get through this without people who'd been there done that. Mike had just lost his closest uncle. My sponsor had lost a number of people in her life. I have one friend who is so strong. She's lost some really important people in her life in a short amount of time. She lives far away but I'd call her when I was having these moments and ask her,

"Is this normal?" I'd listen. We'd talk and pray. Then we'd laugh and say, "Oh, duh. It's grief!" Those friends who'd lost people in their life were like my friends in recovery. They'd walked down this road and understood my pain. I was so grateful to be able to reach out to them for support because I could not do this alone. I'd also listen to people who had great stories of my Dad. It just warms my heart. So does listening to the music that he loved.

He and I shared a love of music ever since I was a little girl driving back and forth between D.C. and Philly with him. Even as an adult, I'd make him mixes for every holiday and he'd call me to tell me how much he loved them or blast them at the beach house in Nantucket. Now I hear a song randomly in the car that reminds me of him and I'll get a big smile and just say, "Hi, Dad!" Other times I make mixes to run to or drive to that remind me he is with me. It's all stuff that keeps me going during this healing time. When I hear an old Bruce Hornsby Song like "Mandolin Rain," or Bruce Springsteen's "Glory Days," or "The Rising" my heart is just filled with joy. I remember standing in a record store in Austin, Texas, with Mike in February 2011 and realizing I was searching for all the old music my Dad and I used to listen to together on our long drives. Fine Young Cannibals, Sting, etc. I had this Healthy Voice moment where I realized this was supposed to be part of my healing. The song "God Gave Me You" is another one that gets me because it reminds me that Dad was a gift to me and still is to my spirit.

There is one special song that reminds me of the connection to Dad I have in nature. It's called "You're Beautiful". It's by Phil Whickam and it came on the radio one day when I was just really missing Dad. I was driving down the road crying my eyes out. I looked to the sky and saw the most beautiful sunset so I just stopped to listen to the song and miss him and the lyrics seems so appropriate for my relationship with Dad and with God. I could take a breath in that moment, and listen for peace through nature's beauty.

Sunsets have become my favorite time to connect with my Dad. I just know he is there and I can talk to him about whatever is going on in my life. He's there in countless other ways—like a butterfly, a single bird on a tree, a calm body of water, a rainbow, a sunrise through the kitchen window or sunrays all lined up peeking through the clouds. Oh, he's there. No doubt about it.

> *"Angels are always nearby, ready to encourage us through inspiration, lighten our hearts, and remind us that where there is life, there is joy."*
> —Terry Lynn Taylo

Facing the Fear by Choosing a Milestones Reunion

> *"I have accepted fear as a part of life—specifically the fear of change . . . . I have gone ahead despite the pounding in the heart that says: turn back."*
> —Erica Jong

We all feel fear and doubt. When it is talking to us and it is loud, we can get scared of it and go deeper into it. I was not about to let that Unhealthy Voice take me down after how far I had come. I started to feel anxious around food. It did not make sense to me. I was at peace with food. In fact the Food Plan was actually a gift because for the first time in my life it was almost hard for me to eat anything. It was keeping me nourished! I remember Mike even saying to me on the drive out east, "I guess you really see that food doesn't have the power now, huh?" He was so right. Thank God my Food Plan kept me on track.

Yet, it didn't shut out the Unhealthy Voice. This event was so huge and my Dad was such a huge part of my life that it was still loud. So I listened in deeper. It made sense. Of course it would attack the food first.

That's my first line of weakness ever since I was a little kid and lost my Dad the first time! Then I got clear on what it was saying, "You won't be able to survive this without food. You didn't survive it as a kid and you won't do it now. You will go back." Yes, not only does it try to get you when you are strong, but it tries to get you when you are weak and tired. That is not something you want to hear when you have been in recovery from an eating disorder and you have just lost your Dad in a shocking way. I was scared. I was not scared enough though to give into it. No way. You do not get that power. I thought of Dad and what he would say in this place. I thought about his struggles with food. I thought about mine. If ever there was a time to walk through this again, it was now. Now I had the strength of him in spirit, the time of the holidays to take a break and the place to go to take care of my Healthy Voice.

I made a decision to go back to Milestones for a "Recharge Retreat" they have for all alumni over the holidays. It was a Godsend on multiple levels. This was the place I needed to be to meet myself like I did in May 2008. I made a choice then to walk a new road. This time I wanted to keep walking that road with a change in my life that wasn't in my control. I had a choice. I could listen to my Unhealthy Voice and numb the pain by going back to my addiction or I could go there and meet myself right where I was at—mentally, emotionally, spiritually, and physically. I love going back there. I do not go back to fix me. I go back to give back and get in tune with me. I knew I had to go deeper at this point in my life. I could either go backwards or forwards. Even with recovery, I knew I was fragile. That is why I chose this time to go back. I knew it was the safest place to be. God gave me everything I needed.

Was it easy? No. Was it what I needed? Yes. Challenged with a relationship to someone I didn't know but had to live with that week, I was on my knees in surrender multiple times a day like I'd never been before. It was truly powerful because it was all I needed to realize how much I need God as the guide in my life. It showed me that I am still not Him, and that is truly a gift. Not only that, I still need other people to not only guide me but walk with me on the journey. I'll never "get this." I'll always be growing, learning and living. Hearing the stories of people who'd lost loved ones that were there made me grateful I came when I did this time. It also made me extremely grateful I came when I did back in 2008. My alumni trip back at Milestones was exactly what I needed to keep my sails going in the right direction.

God and Dad gave me another reminder of that direction just before it was time for me to leave. It was of all places at the grocery store in between the produce section and the bakery. "Free Fallin'" by Tom Petty piped into the loud speakers (one of Dad's old favorites). I looked at the fruit, then over at the cake, and I could hear Dad say almost in union with the song playing, "You are free from that stuff. I am free from it. I am happy. You are happy. You don't need that stuff. Keep being you. Keep choosing you. Keep choosing healthy. Keep empowering you and you will keep empowering others." Then I'm standing over the fruit with some tears streaming down my face, in a good way.

Minutes later, I am walking through the store and I spot a little girl walking through the aisles alone. She looks to be about four years old. Doctors may categorize her as overweight. I don't see that. I see hope. I heard my Healthy Voice say, "That girl does not deserve to grow up with a food addiction. She deserves to live empowered by her Healthy Voice with the knowledge and choices that will help her live more fully." This little girl wandering the store alone, trying to navigate the food aisles by herself is why I am here on this earth. My experiences have given me the ability to empower kids like her and their parents. That girl right there is why I am doing what I am doing. No kid has to numb the feelings they feel. They deserve to live a healthy, happy life without food running their lives.

"My father didn't tell me how to live, he lived, and let me watch him do it."
—Clarence Budinton Kelland

That trip set my feet even more firmly into the direction of my recovery and my path towards God. I wanted Him leading my life because I knew there was no way I could get through it without Him. It helped me see how I do have Dad in my life just in a different place. He's in my heart and not on the phone or in person. I'm going to miss his smiling face and hilarious personality like all get out. I'll miss his calls that used to pump me up for life more than ever. Yes, God may have taken Him before we were ready, but I also see the bright side of how much we healed. I see how many memories I have and how much he taught me. I see how he was just showing the way before he left this earth to what God had planned in the next chapter of life. It's like spending a lifetime three hours away from Dad prepared me for this moment with him in my heart and spirit alone. I never thought God would show me the miracle of the situation that way, but He did in only the way He could and in so doing I felt closer to both of my fathers.

A Step Forward with the Guy in my Life

Dad and God weren't the only men in my life. Mike was still by my side and a total rock for me through every step of losing Dad. The beautiful thing is that I wasn't expecting him to fix the pain as only God can. He could just be present to me, comfort me and help in any way I needed. Funny, he was working on another plan while I was in Florida at Milestones that I didn't know about. He was designing a ring. Yes, we had talked about getting married and thought it would be cool to announce the engagement in Austin when our whole family would be there at this race, but I didn't think he would do it! He did and it was the most beautiful day, weekend, and moment ever. I didn't think for one minute that my Dad wasn't there and just like the moment I lost Dad on August 23rd, I was amazed at how much joy I was feeling! This was the moment every girl dreams of having and Mike had picked the perfect time to do it. I couldn't have planned it better. The end of the Austin Half Marathon he got down on his knee in front of the whole crowd and proposed. He got so quiet I thought he was having the post-race runs. So I pointed to a port-a-pot he could use, but that wasn't the problem. When I notice he was actually speechless for once, and he was getting choked up, I knew something was up. The series of pictures we posted on Facebook that my aunt took captured it moment by moment. It was just awesome. All I could think about was Dad going, "So Mere! Let's get going! Next chapter of your life—I'm gone but let's get this awesome new life with Mike started, okay!"

How funny, I'd planned to do the Austin Half Marathon so we could dedicate the run to my Dad on President's weekend for what would have been his birthday. Then God (and Mike) had another plan. What a weekend! I still can't believe he carried the ring a whole 13.1 miles. Not only that, I had one of the best runs I've ever had in my life—just totally felt my Dad's presence. I had my cousin Ali running her first marathon and we had shirts made for Dad that said, "Isn't this great" on the back and "Powered by Petey" on the front. At one point we were getting ready to go up this massive hill everyone was talking about called Enfield Road and there was this huge display of rays of sun popping through the clouds. Overcome with joy and tears I just said, "Guys look! It's Dad, he's here to take us up the hill!" That he did. I thought it was so cool to be coming full circle—finishing the half marathon with Mike, running through the chute that was stationed right where the stage was on Election Night 2000. It was just an amazing day . . . and then the surprise. Isn't God just great? What's even better is we got to celebrate that night with a few couples that have been in my life and I've admired for how they've led their marriages. I just felt surrounded by hope and pure love. The whole weekend just showed that even though tragedy happens, life goes on and so does joy.

Turning Life Over to my Rock in an Even Deeper Way

"Life is change. Growth is optional. Choose wisely."
—*Unknown*

My rock is the Higher Power I call God and my Dad's death showed me that—big time. Change is inevitable. It's out of our control even though we subconsciously try to control it. All we can do is surrender to the process and do what we can with what we've got. Losing someone you love in an instant is a powerful example of how to practice it. The place I was at in my life when I lost Dad amazes me and still am amazed at the peace of God that I was given. Even though I may question him at times of struggle, I can always remember that He not only got me through recovery, but through my Dad's death. He comforts me in my mourning in a way that no one can, not even Mike. That pain I feel is only for Him to heal and carry me through.

"Blessed are those who mourn, for they shall be comforted."
—*NIV, Matthew 5:4*

I'd sit and work on this book looking out on Lake Michigan or at the trees to calm me down with a sign in front of me with the scripture engraved,

"Be still and know that I am God."
—*NIV, Psalm 46:10*

If I'd ask why, I'd know I wouldn't get the answers because I wasn't supposed to get them. He'd give me the peace to let go. I'd repeatedly look at one of my favorite scriptures realizing why through this experience He had placed this one so prominently in my life.

"Trust in the Lord with all your heart and lean not on your own understanding; in all your ways submit to him, and he will direct your paths."
—NIV, Proverbs 3:5-6

The best part is I know Dad's up there with Him and they've got me covered—big time. Peace during intense pain is a crazy feeling, and it's one I could only give to the grace of God.

That peace reminds me of a song I started to listen to at the time called "One Thing Remains" by Brian Johnson.

God will never stop loving me and He'll never leave me. He never left me when my parents divorced and hasn't left me yet. Never will.

"The Lord is my strength and my shield; my heart trusts in him, and he helps me. My heart leaps for joy, and with my song I praise him."
—NIV, Psalm 28:7

Moving Forward with Purpose

The book I'd started just a week before Dad passed had to keep moving, and so did all the things God had planned for my life, including the bigger purpose. I felt so blessed that I got to share some of God's vision with Dad before he left because it almost felt like he was creating it with me. It hurt like hell not to be able to call him and share it all with him, but I know he's been writing it with me. Not only that, recovery had been my rock through all of this grief. I could also be comforted by both of my parents' inner strength. My Mom told me that Dad lost his Dad at a very young age and going through that made him even more purposeful about his life. Nothing could stop him. That gave me a ton of courage. Even my Mom's faith and courage to endure strengthened me within. Neither of them probably knew how much their enduring faith was helping me get through this time. I knew that this book was part of my purpose. It was something Dad and I had talked about and I wasn't going to give up. This commitment to it wasn't about me. It was about everyone who needed a Healthy Voice.

"But those who hope in the Lord will renew their strength.
They will soar on wings like eagles; They will run and
not grow weary, They will walk and not be faint."
—NIV, Isaiah 40:31

A funny thing happened when I lost Dad. The Healthy Voice in my life became even clearer and I was finding the spirit within my channeling and even more positive attitude and energy towards life. There was no doubt in my mind that Dad's spirit was within me. I realized that life has a way of slowing you down, of showing you that it's really a journey, not a fix. I was writing this book channeling this Healthy Voice realizing there's a roadmap to all of this. So I discovered that roadmap is really "The Journey to your Healthy Voice."

PART IV:
No Better Time to Get on the Journey

CHAPTER SEVENTEEN:

The Journey to Your Healthy Voice

I never realized there was an actual journey until I realized I have to keep meeting myself on it. I share it with you because I hope that you'll use it as a way to get to your Healthy Voice no matter where you are, no matter when. I hope you'll go back to it many times in your life like I do. Finally getting them all down on paper has helped me clarify the journey and I hope it will do the same for you. Remember, these are not the fix. There will be more to them in an action guide that you can really sink your feet into so consider this as getting your feet wet. I wanted to make sure you got the journey concept down. Also, these are NOT a replacement for any therapy, physical, or religious spiritual program you may be involved in. These are just a complement to whatever program you have or do consider trying out. I hope by considering them, you have fun on the journey. I hope you learn a ton about yourself, grow, feel, heal, and all the fun stuff that goes along with it! So without further ado:

The Journey to Your Healthy Voice

1. Be willing to look Beyond the Weight and go Beneath the Surface.
2. Be willing to set your feet in the direction of your Healthy Voice.
3. Surrender to the grace of love and forgiveness.
4. Tap the power of the Healthy Voice Spirit within you.
5. Commit to taking steps forward on the Healthy Voice Journey.
6. Take care of your body by addressing your physical health and practicing your Healthy Voice Food and Fitness Truth.
7. Take care of your mind by addressing your mental and emotional health.
8. Be willing to nurture your feelings and leave the healing process up to God.
9. Use your Unhealthy Voice Navigation System to recognize and learn from triggers.
10. Strengthen your Healthy Voice with the Healthy Voice Navigation Tools.
11. Be willing to share the power of your Healthy Voice Story so that it may help others.
12. Be the Healthy Voice Light for yourself, for another—for the world.

#1. Be willing to look Beyond the Weight and go Beneath the Surface.

Once I started to do all this inner work, I realized the weight didn't have the power it did before. Of course my appearance was important, but when I was working on my spiritual self, the physical self would take care of itself. I wasn't stressing about it or focusing on it. Because I had sought help for that, I could do the other work and leave that piece up to my Higher Power who had given me the tools. Looking at my weight as the "be all" "end all" just didn't make sense anymore. Not only that, I couldn't afford to allow that in my recovery. If I did, I'd be in big trouble because I'd be seeking inner peace on the outside again which could take me back to my eating disorder. Whenever I was troubled, I had to see what was going on in myself. That's something 12-step recovery taught me. Being willing to look beyond the weight is something I had to be committed to, even on the days when I felt fat! Knowing I was more than a physical being helped, so did knowing I had faulty brain chemistry, a disease of the mind and body, and a spiritual program. These were all tools that helped me be in that place! If I got to that place of thinking it was about the weight, I had to be willing to look beyond it to what was really going on. I challenge you to look at what's really going on instead of driving yourself insane always looking at the weight. What is it deflecting you from? Looking at the weight is just a lame excuse for that Unhealthy Voice to distract you and convince you that your self-worth is only in your physical. You may need to lose weight, but that process will never give you your self-worth. You've got to find that inside by going beneath the surface.

#2: Be willing to set your feet in the direction of your Healthy Voice.

I can't just believe that I'm not going to think about the weight obsessively. I have to set my feet in the direction of my Healthy Voice.

I have to choose not to focus on all of that. I have to let go of the story I have been hanging on to and staring at for years, that's been keeping me addicted to food or diets. I have to recognize my Unhealthy Voice wants me to follow its lead so in order to not do that, I literally have to change my direction. I have to change the course of the ship. I have to decide that I'm not going to just lose the weight to lose it. I'm going to lose it to change my lifestyle—to make it a journey. I have to change my approach and perspective to the Healthy Voice otherwise I'll be doing the same thing I've done before.

I have to have faith that if I set my feet in the right direction, the Lord will carry me. The Pastor at my church uses a simple metaphor that reminds me of this. If you put your feet in one direction, you are walking towards God. If you put them in the other direction, you are walking away from God. It's simple as that. Whatever point I'm at in my life, I can do this. Sometimes it may not seem like a clear path, but if I just have a little faith and remember I can put my trust in Him, I can relax and remember He's the boss. All I have to look at is everything He's already done. Even if I have very little faith in myself to do something or trust in Him to carry me through, He's there.

> *"I tell you the truth, if you have faith as small as a mustard seed, you can say to the mountain, 'Move from here to there' and it will move. Nothing will be impossible for you.'"*
>
> —*NIV, Matthew 17:20*

#3: Surrender to the grace of love and forgiveness.

It can be hard to surrender, especially when we don't trust, we've been hurt, or we don't think there is a power greater than us to handle it. Every day I turn to God and pray for his strength as the one who is leading my life. His power is greater than mine in all things. This was not always the case. I used to pray with nothing in me. Now I just trust, even on those days when I feel like He isn't listening.

No matter what I feel, he is always there ready to fill me up with love. Not only that, he forgives. That's why he died on the cross so I could live fully on earth. For me to hold onto something makes no sense, because no matter how much I don't like myself for it, there is nothing I could do that could make him love me any more or any less. He just does.

Surrender gets a bad rap. People think that it's giving up. Willpower has gotten way too much power. Willpower is necessary, but it doesn't have all the power. Being surrendered humbles me. It helps me know that I'm not all that powerful, that I can't control people, places, and things, and helps me keep my ego in check. I am grateful that I can surrender to a power that is greater than me and receive the grace that is there for me if I just ask for it. In the beginning of my spiritual walk it was the Serenity Prayer, and it still is a huge part of my life. Yet in my walk with Christ, this scripture has also been a huge part of receiving that grace. I have a completely new understanding of it. I used to feel guilty about His death on the cross. Now I know it happened so that I could live. That is some powerful stuff.

> *"I have been crucified with Christ. It is no longer I who live, but Christ who lives in me. And the life I now live in the flesh I live by faith in the Son of God, who loved me and gave himself for me."*
> —*NIV, Galatians 2:20*

#4: Tap the power of the Healthy Voice Spirit within you.

Once you realize it's not just about the weight and not just about willpower, you find that there is this spirit inside of you. It's a spirit you knew you always had but never knew how to name. You see it in people who inspire you. Now you can. The beauty is that there is no "right" way to do it. All you've got to do is recognize that the power that is greater than you, that created you—has developed a spirit inside of you that I like to call the Healthy Voice Spirit because it can ignite the fire for your whole journey. It can inspire you physically, mentally, and emotionally from the spiritual place that takes you to a whole new level. I found it when I realized that working out couldn't just be about the fix and going to church couldn't be just about the duty. I found it when I got in recovery, and when I lost my Dad. I find it every day. It's awesome. The most important thing about it is that I found that it's within me and all I've got to do is tap into it. I've just got to get quiet or go to my peaceful place to recognize it, and I'm good to go. It means I don't have to get the best body, the best workout, or the best anything to be enough. I've got more than enough in me. Everything else is just a bonus. I would not have found this if I hadn't gotten off the road of "the fix" and into the journey. It means that no matter how tough things are emotionally or how tough something is physically, it's that spirit within me that I can tap into to carry me. It gives me a strength I never knew I had. For me, that higher power strength is God. He is my greatest Healthy Voice. I don't know what it will be for you, but I hope that you find it and start to tap into it in every aspect of your life.

"For God did not give us a spirit of timidity, but a spirit of power, of love and of self-discipline."
—NIV, 2 Timothy 1:7

#5: Commit to taking steps forward on the Healthy Voice Journey.

Steps come on at a time –at least that's what I've learned in recovery. We tend to look at the road ten miles or years down the road and get overwhelmed. The journey is overwhelming. Yet it doesn't have to be. It can actually be comforting. It can actually help us realize that we don't need fixing, that we can commit to ourselves, to our bodies, our minds and our spirits for the long haul. By committing to taking a step forward, we're committing to ourselves really. When you realize you've got the power within you, don't you just want to can get out of trying to fix yourself? I know I did, and I do every time I'm trying to do something on my own or I need to tap into that spiritual strength within me. He's meeting me halfway now, not expecting me to get good enough. I have to remind myself of that regularly because it's not what I always thought. When I do, it's a huge sense of relief!

Another reason I have to commit to taking the steps forward is because I know my Unhealthy Voice is always going to be there to tempt me. I can't stuff it down with emotional eating or turn it off with a diet. It doesn't go away, even though I tried to make it do that for years. When I look at the horizon ahead, the road to my Healthy Voice looks brighter than my Unhealthy Voice. Of course my Unhealthy Voice will toss the potholes and storms, but the road ahead isn't cloudy forever. There is always a light through the storms.

I just know which road I want to choose.

I have made the choice in my life to follow my Healthy Voice. I know that I do not have it all figured out. I know that I have to commit to the journey and rely on my higher power for strength each day that He gives me. I don't just get my Healthy Voice. I have to choose it every day. It has to be intentional.

CHAPTER 18:

Addressing my Physical Health

"Do you not know that your bodies are temples of the Holy Spirit, who is in you, who you have received from God? You are not your own;"
—NIV, 1 Corinthians 6:19-20

If you've been paying attention to the last few steps on the journey, you may have a light bulb going off in your head realizing how this passage now makes sense. You may also be conflicted with the way society has taken the idea of the body as a temple to a whole other level. What I see in every age group and facet of society is people thinking that God wants you to lose the weight. Well, of course God wants you to be healthy in your body because He gave it to you to live in, but it's not His main purpose for you, on this earth. We think God wants us to be skinny if he's telling us we should make it a temple, right? No, that's something we've made up in our own minds because we've seen them on runways. We think God wants us to have these extremely fit bodies so we can be worshipped. Not so much. Being fit is awesome! I love feeling strong in my body! I admire people who have a commitment to a serious workout program, 6-packs to showcase or a serious race time. More power to you! Making our bodies our gods though, is where we've gone overboard. That's not what I think was intended any more than worshiping those people who've lost the weight or have the 6-packs. We've got to just value our own bodies we've have and in order to get to that place we've got to tune into our Healthy Voice!

The Healthy Voice Perspective on addressing your physical health is all about finding balance, paying attention to what your body needs for health reasons, and maintaining good health with eating habits and regular exercise.

#6: Take care of your body by addressing your physical health and practicing your Healthy Voice Food and Fitness Truth.

What Do You Have to Work With?

Many of us have physical health issues like hypertension and diabetes that doctors can relate back to our excess weight. I've seen people drop their BMI numbers and their diabetes medication by simply dropping pounds and changing their behaviors. It is not joke that lifestyle change is a huge factor when it comes to our physical health. I can certainly say I was scared when I found out from my doctor in early recovery that I had high blood sugar and barely touched it at all! It sure made me grateful that recovery took me off of it as a regular habit. It also made me remember that my grandmother had diabetes. It also helped me to be more conscious of my choices—instead of making me the helpless victim. I am a firm believer that you can reverse these kinds of genetic trends within yourself if you make some simple behavior changes.

The point is that we always have to be willing to address our physical health. I don't care if it's our teeth, our skin, blood pressure, weight, or what have you. A lot of times our internal struggles show up in our physical bodies and often times addressing whatever issue is on the table can help us get through it, but the work doesn't stop there.

The Discipline Behind a Healthy Lifestyle

Through all my years of dieting from the age of seven to thirty-one and all those miles I logged training, I learned the practice of a physical self-discipline. It took miles of walking before I ever ran a mile. It took many salads before I ever actually preferred whole foods over processed. Being physically healthy requires discipline. It requires a commitment to eating a balanced diet and maintaining regular physical activity. That is not easy when it's not a regular habit. It got even harder when I had to go to treatment and learn a whole new way of practicing this physical discipline. I'd spent so many years making up my own rules with diets and running my brains out that I thought I knew my truth—until I found out that I was in the extreme zone. My Eating Disorder was making up the crazy food rules; even telling myself that I had to run off the calories I was consuming. Nothing about my choices was my own, but learning from those who knew better than me at how to practice new behaviors to fuel my body with food and fitness allowed me to learn new disciplines. It took practice to get the hang of it and it still takes commitment. My discipline with running was unhealthy. They helped me find a balance with it. My food obsession was over the top. They helped me get out of that. Thank God I got the help I needed to get me out of my physical self-discipline because it wasn't working! Yet, I have to commit to it every single day!

My Truth

I did not get fixed when I went to treatment. There is no program that fixes you out there. It addresses your physical, but it won't fix you because you've still got to live your life. I have to fight every day to keep my body in shape and my body fueled. I don't fight for a fit body. I maintain a healthy body. I can't do that by anyone's definition of healthy. I have to love my body and work from that space to keep it healthy. I can't be obsessed with working out. I have to work with the turtle speed metabolism handed down to me through generations by working out and not choosing foods that will land on my thighs or stomach. Believe me, I've tried to eat like my friends who can eat just about anything. It doesn't work. Am I freakishly healthy eater? No. I actually try to take the focus off my food because I believe everyone is just too obsessed with it. We all need to find our own plan and stick to it so we can get to all the good stuff in our lives. Stop talking about it! I'd rather talk about how I'm navigating the food triggers or how I didn't choose the trigger snack or how I messed up! I don't want to talk about how I'm walking in the lines perfectly. I want to talk about how I'm being human about it. I'm fine with not being a "normal" eater (whatever that is!) I'm comfortable with the fact that I am a food addict and I accept that I am not going to be able to sit down and plow through an extra-large sundae on the couch or a huge bag of chips for my nighttime snack. It just can't happen. Food is my fuel and food can be enjoyable, but it can't answer my prayers. Again, I've tried. It doesn't work.

The Creation of the Food and Fitness Truth

At first this was something that helped me tune into the things that I need to physically take care of myself. Then I found myself recommending it to people. They would ask me to help them lose weight, and I'd challenge them to find their truth because the last thing I was going to do was tell them how to lose weight. That's your own physical journey. There were enough of those and my job was to go within. But I can become willing to guide them to their truth because so many of my clients were so scattered from years of dieting, reading magazines, and reading diets books. They didn't know which end was up! Yet finding peace helped them get grounded so they could find what they need, not what everyone else was telling them they needed to do about it. This gives you an idea of my truth. It is always changing as my relationship with both food and exercise changes but here's where it's at in the first edition of my book.

My Food Truth

When it comes to food, I use it as fuel for living and nourishment. It is no longer this huge emotional crutch that I need to carry me throughout my days. I know when it comes to food I have to do three things: 1) stick to my own personal food plan, 2) shop for and choose my go-to foods, 3) know my triggers, 4) be gentle on myself, and recognize that 5) food is not a topic for judgment, emotional, or political warfare.

I've got a plan and you've got yours. I know God's will for me was to have a Food Plan. It does not work for everyone. It works for me. It does exactly what I need it to do to keep me on the path of recovery. It keeps me physically nourished, mentally stable, and emotionally balanced. Most of all, it allows me to be present for life. It allows me to always make the healthy choice in a very simple way wherever I am and whatever I'm doing, I can always make a healthy choice with what's available. I remain accountable to it by weighing and measuring my food on a food scale as well as using cups and spoons for measurement when I have my scale. I have no shame about that. Being someone who has the disease of "more" in a society where portions are the size of Texas, I know where my addiction can take me. I'd rather use the tools I've been given. I am not afraid of things like fat, carbohydrates, proteins, or my daily calorie intake because I trust my nutritionist. These are tools from God. I trust that if I do not have the ability to use them, He will guide me to do the next right thing and I will make the right choice because I've got Him with me. It absolutely does not mean I do it perfectly—far from it. Yet, it's the way that I remain accountable to my physical self so I don't have to get obsessed about my body, the scale, or some diet again.

My Healthy Voice Go-To Foods keep me sane and grounded. I shop for the foods at the store that are my basics. They are not boring and I don't eat the same thing every day. It's not complicated and everything is easy to make. I'm grateful I learned how to cook so many recipes in treatment with whole foods. I never feel deprived and always feel empowered when I find myself creating a new recipe. It's even better when someone says, "Wow, that's really good!" Yes, I'm not on a diet and I don't deprive myself of the good stuff. I just choose the good stuff. It's awesome! I don't worry about what someone else is thinking as far as what they can and can't eat because that's their truth. I worked hard to find mine and did some serious surrendering, so I'm going to keep doing what works for me. I never tell people what to eat and once they get into asking what they should eat all I can say is, seek a professional. I thank God I did not go down the path of becoming one because I think I'd go nuts if I were prescribing food plans. Drinking lots of water every day is very important to me because I can get dehydrated quick from exercise. Eating protein at breakfast is hugely important. Carrying a snack with veggie and protein is just as important and being prepared with a meal in the case there may not be one is always good. You will always see me getting on a flight with some sort of food because I am not touching the stuff they have available in transit. I try to prepare my meals and snacks if I'm not going to be at home writing and I even try to prepare my meals at the beginning of the week so I can create with stuff that's already made. Preparation and planning is HUGE!

My triggers are there. The more aware of them I am, the better off I am. I know that they don't always come from food. I know they can come from stress, from situational triggers, from exhaustion and just about anything else. Yet if I'm present to myself and learn from each one I can walk through them with the grace of a loving higher power.

Food police do not have to occupy my mind anymore. I choose to not beat myself up in them. I used to beat the crap out of my body. I'd run so many miles, eat so much food and drink so much alcohol in such a short amount of time. Then I'd go back to extreme dieting and excess running just a few days later. My poor body didn't know what hit it. I don't do that anymore. I'm gentle on my body. If my body needs restorative yoga, that's what it needs. If my body needs to walk, I walk. I embrace my rest days instead of fight the urge to jump out of my skin. I can challenge it but I don't have to beat it up if it didn't reach my goals. I don't have to beat it up with the Unhealthy Voice that likes to get me in my mind when I run. I can also take care of it when it needs healing from an injury. These are all gifts.

I have to remember that God is not standing over me anymore with a stick saying, "When you lose the weight, you'll be good enough Meredith." No. He loves me no matter what my weight is and he will never make His love conditional on a scale, a BMI prediction, or let it fall on what someone else says about it. I may need to do something about it because of what a professional says but that does not mean God loves me any less. He is NOT a punishing God in my book and he certainly is not using food to punish me. That's the devil in my book. It's the devil that tells me to get my body perfect or my food perfect so that I can have everything under control. It is God who gives me a Food Plan that I can use to keep me grounded and it is God that carries me through the moments when I struggle with food. I cannot beat myself up about what I eat. There are no "shouldn't" and there is no shame. There is only victory. When I get off track, I don't get out my personal Gestapo. I get accountable with my food, my sponsor, myself, and I get back on track. I do not diet. I let my Healthy Voice be the gentle loving God that guides me through life.

The politics of food is not up for debate with me. Recognize that food is a fuel for living in my life, not a topic for judgment, emotional, or political warfare. Food is fuel for me. Period. I work very hard at not getting into any debate about what is the "right" way because I know there isn't one. I simply do what works for me and go about my business. It relieves me of a lot of stress and chaos. I spent years using food as an emotional weapon for getting what I want in life. No more. I spent two years knee-deep in the politics of food and obesity in government and it's not where I belong. I don't care if you are on Capitol Hill, in a diet center, or in a circle with your friends—your food choices are your choices. It is one of the most personal issues known to man and we've let it become one of the most chaotic, revealing, controversial, political, and volatile issues around. I don't touch it. If you are in the politics of food then more power to you. Yet getting into a debate with your friends is pointless—at least that's what I've learned. My food truth is my food truth. Simple as that. We all walk different paths—whether it's a diet, a Food Plan, or whatever. Judging others does not help. Leading by example does. I've got my plan so I just keep walking the path and letting others have their field day with what they think everybody should or shouldn't be eating.

My Fitness Truth

This is pretty simple for me because I can't go to the extreme of not working out nor can I go to the extreme of obsessive working out. The obsession of exercising is thankfully, no longer a part of me. I've got to find a balance. I've got to find a variety of activities that keep me grounded in a physical practice that keeps me physically, mentally, emotionally, and spiritually healthy. I'm finally free from the rigid obsession with one workout, a certain amount of calories burned or time clocked. Exercise for me has become a meaningful part of my life. I believe it's because I had to find this new relationship with it. I love finding new exercises and doing pretty much anything that moves my body but I know that these things that I share speak to my truth so I rely on these for physical strength:

- Running or Hiking
- Yoga
- Cycling
- Resistance or weight training

With each one of these I have a variety of approaches and I'm always open to new things or new types of exercise. The thing I've found with these is they all help me stay out of my head and that's what I need when it comes to exercise. Not only that, the way I approach them keeps me disciplined and excited. It's truly amazing how doing just a few simple activities with a variety of approaches can help tune you into your Healthy Voice Truth. The variety of ways I approach them gives me a gift beyond anything I could imagine in a purely physical way. With each one of these approaches I can find one or more of the following:

Each one reminds me of the journey. As a former marathon runner, I'm very familiar with the concept of life not being a sprint but a marathon. I didn't truly grasp it until I got into recovery. When I did, I realized that much like everything else in my life, I wanted my fitness choices to reflect the journey. So I found a healthier relationship with running. I took up road cycling. I did more yoga. Through each of these, I found that they reflected the concept of the journey. You could always get on the road and run. You could always get into the rhythm of your bike ride and you could always come back to the mat. Each one of them reminded me that I could meet myself and my body wherever I was at that day. Each one, like a trusted friend keeps me inspired for the long haul. My body is what carries me for the journey and I need to keep it strong!

I can tap into my Healthy Voice Spirit. When I work out, I truly commune with the spirit of God. It is absolutely no longer a fix for me. It's amazing how once you tune into the rhythm you can find that power that is greater than you just by a repeated movement. It's truly moving meditation. If the road gets rough or the yoga pose is difficult to hold, I can remember that God's spirit is carrying me. "I can do all things with Christ who strengthens me." Philippians 4:13. Every time I get on a bike, whether I'm inside or outside, I get into the rhythm enough that I can tune into his spirit because he will carry me through the journey. Just relying on my physical willpower makes me want to beat myself up but with the spirit of God, I can do anything. It makes me think of the 2012 Olympics when so many Christians were participating and proclaiming their love for God. I would watch them and not be inspired by their physical strength alone. I'd be inspired by how strong their trust in God must be. Then I'd hear them speak after winning a gold medal and I'd just go, "That right there is a Healthy Voice." For example, Gabby Douglas, the young gymnast blew me away with her humility and love for God when she won the gold for Women's All Around Gymnast, "I give all the glory to God. It's kind of a win-win situation. The glory goes up to Him, and the blessings fall down on me." I may never be one of them, but I feel like we're on the journey together and that inspires me. If she can do it, I can do it if I put my willpower and trust God's faith in my ability!

All can be done in nature. This is when I feel truly alone with the spirit of God. I struggle sometimes with going to a gym. I'd rather be outside in nature than on a machine inside any day. I struggle too with people who are going to the gym for purely physical fix reasons. It reminds me of who I used to be so going outside reminds me of who I am today. It reminds me that God is so much bigger than me. It also allows me to just take in everything around me. I absolutely love it. If there is good scenery, even better. There is nothing better than a beautiful run or a bike ride through the countryside. I love a yoga class by the water too. There is nothing more refreshing.

All can be done with music. Music is such a huge part of my life, especially motivational music that inspires you to have a great run. I love when someone teaches a spin class with fabulous music or I go to a yoga class and the music speaks to me so much in that moment that it brings me to tears. Moving your body while you listen to music is an emotional experience and I love it! When I find my groove with my tunes, or the playlist surprises me with some really inspiring song right when I'm coming around the corner—it's a total Healthy Voice Moment.

Participating in community events around them reminds me I'm not on the journey alone. When we think of a fitness community, so many of us are one of two extremes. We think we can't ever go into a gym because we're too embarrassed. If not that, we think we have to compete with everyone else in the community there. What I've found is power in the fitness community. I've found that when I go to a spin or yoga class or if I go run a 10K, I'm excited to share in the journey with people. We are all coming to the start line together or taking the class together. We are all in it together! It's a gift! So I not only participate in regular community events like rides and races, but I have the studios I go to and the website I go to at home that feels like a community where I can do my yoga. I love running around Town Lake in Austin because the running community there is just so huge. You are running alone but you don't feel like it at all as nature, trails, and people surround you everywhere. It's awesome!

I remember that I'm running my own race. I can run my own race, ride my own bike, hike my own trail, and stay on my own mat. No matter what happens during my workout, or who crosses my path—it's always still just my journey. I don't have to worry about what someone else is doing by comparing or competing. I can just keep running my own race.

"Let us run with perseverance the race marked out for us."
—NIV, Hebrews 12:1

The Healthy Voice Workout

When you are tuned into your Healthy Voice Spirit, it's truly a mind, body, and spirit experience. You get to find the power of it in your workout but then experience it in so many different ways. Just like the weight, the workout fix, or reading the calories on the machine just doesn't have the power it did. I get on spin bikes now or I read my Garmin and I'm so much more focused on my breath, the scenery or the rhythm of the bike wheels, it's not even funny! The best part is you find it on your own, with your own activities, your own music, your own approaches, and any variety of them in your life. By approaching workouts like this, you never have to see the workout as a chore or a fix again. It's about total connection to your Healthy Voice Spirit. Once you start to tune into it, you find that you have these multi-sensory experiences more regularly. I'm sometimes amazed at the Healthy Voice Workout Moments I have when everything seems so synchronized! Imagine running towards the end of a road that leads toward a beach with a beautiful sunset and the song that inspires you the most comes on your playlist right when you are approach the beach. It happens to me all the time! It can literally bring you to tears how powerfully everything can come together. It doesn't even have to be in nature. It can be in a spin class or on a yoga mat and you will be blown away. I can't tell you how many times I've come to the yoga mat and found myself in tears of gratitude at the end of class while in Shavashna or corpse pose. Every experience is just this burst of love from the power of God. I can't wait to see with every workout what God's has in store for me on the workout journey. If you start having these experiences, consider yourself a Healthy Voice Athlete! Then start looking for those friends in your life and athletes in the professional field who've got it in them too! You'll be amazed at how much it inspires you.

CHAPTER NINETEEN:

Addressing my Mental and Emotional Health

There is something about willpower that makes us think we have to control our minds and emotions. That's why we go to magazines to find answers for our emotional eating and why we want to learn everything possible from the experts so we can control our minds. My mind is a battlefield (in the words of Joyce Meyer). It's a neighborhood that can be pretty dangerous for me. If I didn't address it when I did, I was headed for trouble. What I found amazing when I did reach out for help is that the connection between my physical and mental health was virtually untapped. All those years I'd struggled with my weight and then started to struggle with my mental health—we never made the connection of the two. Society is so focused on fixing the physical and not wanting to focus on addressing the mental, that there is a virtual lack-of-knowledge-desert about it in our society. That's why I've given it its own step in the journey, because a lot of times when I'm off track—the problem is centered in my mind. Not everyone has mental health issues to combat, but everyone's got an Unhealthy Voice now and then.

#7: Take care of your mind by addressing your mental and emotional health.

Just like the food was a gateway to my Unhealthy Voice as a kid, addressing my mental health was a gateway to whole health for me. It helped me finally get on the road to wellness and find my much needed, Healthy Voice. Getting the help from doctors that knew better than me what to do with my brain chemistry and mind, helped me get on the right path. They helped me work through my emotional health that I had been stuffing down with food and other things for years. My mental health is a crucial part, if not the keystone of my physical health. It affects my functioning, my eating, my relationships, and my self-esteem, everything! The difference is when I addressed it in treatment from the counseling attempts before is that we finally brought it all together. We finally addressed the root of the problem by addressing how my mental health was showing up in my food and behaviors. It wasn't about the food. What I thought was always my weight, was my mind's reaction to my feelings about my parents' divorce when I was a kid. My mind therefore responded to everything like that. I had been conditioned by this addiction and the Unhealthy Voice it had brewed up in me to always react to life, to respond emotionally, and to live in the shadow of my Unhealthy Voice. Dropping the food and alcohol drug and getting the help from mental health professionals that I needed is what arrested it. I thank God for those people at Milestones for knowing how it all fit together, and knowing exactly how to address it.

The beauty of where I went to treatment is that the spiritual program is a part of it. We didn't go there to get a food plan. Dr. Marty Lerner, PhD emphasized the need for a spiritual program, for without God, it's just a diet. From day one that spiritual program was a part of it. That helped me to recognize that it wasn't all about the label of my eating disorder, my food addiction, or my anxiety. Whatever my doctor told me I had going on in my mind, that didn't define me. It's how they defined within scientific terms what was going on in my brain. It helped them address how to treat it and helped me understand that I couldn't do it alone. Having that spiritual program though, kept me out of thinking it was something I had to make sense of or beat myself up about because I needed to lean on God. He was going to carry me through this and little did I know, He was going to want me to share my story so He could carry others through their own recovery journey.

Become Willing to Treat It

Those of us that struggle have to be brave in the face of a society that stigmatizes it. I hope with time, this changes because too many people are suffering and you can't see it. They may look great on the outside, but they are dying inside. It breaks my heart at how much we treat what may be a mental problem with a diet because too many of us don't know there is another way. Weight-loss is all we know. Mental and emotional baggage loss is what many of us actually need. I thank God I had supportive parents who sent me to treatment at this time. Many kids don't and I hope my work can help whoever struggles to find their way to that place if they need it.

I just know that when God gave me the strength to call Milestones I wasn't worry about the stigma. I needed help. I had to do the work when I was there. They didn't fix me. I read books that helped me understand it better. I made playlists that nurtured my healing process. I spent time in nature reflecting. I wrote in a journey a lot and took notes on everything I was learning. I wanted to know more about what made me tick so that I could be more empowered to live! I participated in both group and individual therapy and support groups to help me get out of that Unhealthy Voice that was controlling my mind. Also, the food plan that Nikki prescribed me was the grounding thing that was allowing me to be present to all of this.

Discipline with Mental Health

My mental health discipline is just as important as the physical. Going to treatment did not "fix" me anymore than finding out I suffered from Binge Eating Disorder did. I am certainly in recovery but I do not believe I'm recovered because I will always have a physical disease in my body and allergy in my mind. Yet, that's not a bad thing, for it allows me to approach treatment as a lifestyle rather than a fix. So in order for me to stay in recovery, I need to practice those things that replace my disease behaviors. I need to be careful of the things in life that I go through (like loss) and know that I'm going to be a little more fragile or quick to want to fix it with a drug of some kind. When I'm under stress, I'm vulnerable to it. When I'm physically exhausted, I'm vulnerable. When I'm overly hungry, I'm vulnerable. Thinking I'm fixed is what gets me stuck. I'm not going to pretend I can will myself to it. I've seen the pictures of my brain chemistry makeup. I know it's genetic. I know I can't squeeze out the serotonin through my brain. It's not something I can do with a diet. I know that my Dad's death seriously affected it and I've needed to address it. I've needed to go to counseling again, but that is okay because I understand that it's necessary when you are going through certain things in your life. If I'm willing, I'll be able to walk through it with God.

I will always need God, the tools, and people he's given me to walk this life. The longer I stay in recovery, the stronger I get physically, mentally, emotionally, and spiritually. Part of taking care of it is using the tools of my 12-step recovery and going to meetings to talk about that disease of the mind and body. It's using the food plan and the food scale that keeps me out of thinking about food. It's being accountable with people in the program. It's being accountable with mental health professionals and honest with my sponsor when I need to be if something doesn't seem right. I encountered this in recovery after Dad passed not realizing my depression was coming back. I always thought I could fight through it but my body would become physically exhausted and my mind would be extra tough to fight. Because of this willingness to take care of it, I could talk to my doctor who worked with many who had gone through this. I could talk to my friend who had been through it and sought medical help and then I could talk to a counselor to help me work through the old stuff that was coming back up as a result of the trauma. Trauma is trauma and we need to work through it when it arises so we don't have to let the disease in our minds take us right back to where we were. This way, we can keep moving forward. Walk through it rather than against it is what I believe I need to do. Yes, it would be nice if I was someone who could just deal with it and I wish mental health was something you could see written on your head so people might have a little more compassion for it, but you can't so that means I just have to be more responsible for my own and that's okay too. So I do what I need to do. I focus on getting help and I do the little things like listen to music. I do the big things like communicate in my relationships, working out, and staying motivated in my work to inspire others.

My Higher Power's Huge Role

As someone who thinks too much and overanalyzes, there is another reason I need God in my life because I can't spend all my time focusing on the mental aspect of my health. It makes me glad I'm not a scientist even more than I'm glad I'm not a nutritionist, because I'd probably make myself nuts. I thank God for the experts in this field who can do all the work and research to help those of us who need it. I certainly seek their help and look forward to more inroads and research in the area of mental health because it only advances the cause of those who don't know it's even a factor. Yet, I can't let it stop there. God protects my mind. When I'm in my head especially, I have got to turn it over to Him. In a world where mental health is rarely treated equally, I trust that God loves all of us equally and He doesn't just heal my heart or my body, He heals my mind and He loves my mind. His power can heal my mind and those people who help me professionally or personally are gifts from Him. When I'm really stuck, it's my faith in God that I can turn to and remember I am His and I'm okay. It's His will that I can always seek and His word to help me overcome this mind of mine.

If I am trying to focus on God's plan and doing God's will in my life, my Unhealthy Voice has a way of trying to derail me from that. All I have to do is start focusing on something else to get distracted—"Squirrel!" That's why focusing on whatever God's will is helps me so much because no matter how distracted I get, I can always come back to where He's got me. It's just a matter of fact that I'm going to get distracted in life. I'm human. Thank God I have some tools because there are just too many ways for us to be stuck in our heads with our Unhealthy Voice. I am thankful for my life coach training with Martha Beck and Byron Katie's "The Work" for helping me through a lot of this.

These are just some of the ways I can get caught up in my mind:

- Thinking about what I've been through which can go into self-pity or blame if not caught
- Worrying about a messy house instead of focusing on the task at hand
- Worrying about what someone else thinks or how they are going to react
- Focusing on feelings of being judged or fearing what others might thinking
- Worrying about someone we love in pain and thinking we know the solution
- Thinking I have to be responsible for someone else's feelings or responsibilities
- All the little and big things I want to achieve that I'm not achieving yet! (Perfectionist)
- Everything I'm not doing and everyone else is (Comparing)

- Everything I don't have yet and need to achieve to meet my expectations of myself (Perfectionism and Self-Reliance)
- Putting the high expectations I put on myself or someone I love
- Fear of the future and focusing on what I'm not doing right now to meet it
- Having to do finances or thinking about what I would do with money if I had it
- Thinking or talking about someone I have a resentment towards (Gossip)
- Fantasizing about what the future might look like
- Thinking I can't get started with my life or project until all these things are squared away—seriously?

Do you see common themes? Fear, worry, self-pity, blame, gossip, and fantasizing. What do all of these things do? Keep me totally distracted from God's will. They keep me from really just living in the NOW. In fact, they keep me absolutely STUCK in one big mental fart. I am not in action. I am not focused on the abundance in my life. I'm focused on the lack and where I'm not enough or the world isn't enough. I am not focused on gratitude. I am not trusting God as much as I should and calling all these things out helps me to recognize the little ways I forget to trust him so I can remember, "Oh! That's my Unhealthy Voice trying to get me to be in my will instead of God's again." I can learn from each one instead and get stronger for the journey ahead, becoming more focused—instead of more derailed. The more focused I get, the more in tune to my Healthy Voice I become.

Here's how easily I can turn those around to hear my Healthy Voice and counter my Unhealthy Voice to be an outright lie. They feel so much better.

- I'm letting go of the past and leaving it there, trusting God's healing process

- I'm getting to my messy house in a disciplined manner at an appropriate time
- What someone else thinks of me is none of my business.
- Only God can work through the chains of someone we love.
- I am only responsible for my own actions and feelings. If someone seeks me for help, I can respond but continue to be responsible for my own life.
- I can stay on top of the little things I have to do in a timely manner.
- I can have goals but leave the outcomes up to God in his perfect timing.
- I can get off Facebook and remember that I'm running my own race
- I have life in abundance. It is crazy how many blessings I have. I don't have to rely on myself or meet my old expectations of myself. God is my co-pilot now and I can trust that he will provide me the help I need when I seek it.
- I can let someone I love be who they are and drop any expectations (because that is just ugly). We can love each other for who we are.
- I do not have to fear the future and stay stuck. God has great plans for me so I can get into action NOW!
- I can be responsible for my finances now, so I can meet my financial goals and be grateful that my riches are in God and relationships, not in material things.
- It's a waste of my time to be thinking or talking about someone and it isn't kind.
- I can allow grief to come and go but I can remember that Dad is with me.

Get excited about the future and create plans but don't get stuck there because that's God's plan Meredith. Be where your feet are!

LIFE IS NOW!

On the journey, I've been amazed about how much scripture says about the way my mind works. It has helped me tremendously in those moments where turning it over to my Higher Power or doing what I'm used to doing just doesn't work.

I can remember that He is transforming my mind. All I have to do is commit to the renewal of it in His will:

> *"Do not conform any longer to the pattern of this world, but be transformed by the renewing of your mind. Then you will be able to test and approve what God's will is –his good, pleasing and perfect will."*
> —*NIV, Romans 12:2*

I can think positive, Wow, who knew?

> *"Finally, brothers and sisters, whatever is true, whatever is noble, whatever is right, whatever is pure, whatever is lovely, whatever is admirable –if anything is excellent and praiseworthy—think about such things."*
> —*NIV, Philippians 4:8*

He doesn't want me to be anxious about anything (wow I could have used that one at the White House):

> *"Do not be anxious about anything, but in every situation, by prayer and petition, with thanksgiving, present your requests to God."*
> —*NIV, Philippians 4:6*

He doesn't want me to worry about results or tomorrow. He just wants me to stay in today. There it is again!

"Therefore do not worry about tomorrow, for tomorrow will worry about itself. Each day has enough trouble of its own."
—*NIV, Matthew 6:34*

My Unhealthy Voice loves fear and His love drives it out. I just have to trust that He is my Healthy Voice!

"There is no fear in love. But perfect love drives out fear, because fear has to do with punishment. The one who fears is not made perfect in love."
—*NIV, John 4:18*

#8: Be willing to nurture your feelings and leave the healing process up to God.

So many of us don't want to feel our feelings or can't identify them. That's probably why we want to control them. We also live in a society that sends the message of "Have it all together, or else." Sharing your feelings can almost be a sign of weakness, but not on the Healthy Voice Journey! That doesn't mean we are being led by feelings. It does mean we acknowledge our feeling along the growing and learning process. It can be tough to finally recognize those feelings we've been stuffing down for a long time, so if you have a little crying spell as you discover things, then you are entitled to it! It's your journey!

The reason I say leave the healing process up to God is because I've found that I can't heal myself. I feel. He heals. When I'm hurting really bad, only He can heal in His time. That is not the fault of humanity or the ones I love. It's just how we were designed. We were designed to rely on and turn to God in our deepest need. Society has tried to distract us and get us to turn to things like food, clothes, and material wealth to satisfy it, but I've found and been inspired by others who seek His love in their heart as well. They may dress nicely but they know that the things that they possess are not what make them okay. It's tough to realize that, but eventually, we can be okay with feeling our feelings! We don't have to cover everything up! Someone can be there for me as I walk through with them but, they aren't going to make them go away. Only God can do that with His great love and timing. I love that. You know why? Because I know that no matter what, I have a source of unconditional love to fill me up. I don't have to worry about being alone to get through. It's a beautiful part of who I am! I don't have to be ashamed of them or hide them.

Here are some of the ways the Unhealthy Voice makes me feel when it lies:

- Feeling hurt or judged by another
- Feeling abandoned
- Feeling worthless or not enough compared to others
- Feeling unworthy of the calling on my life
- Feeling like I'm alone

My feelings could go on and on. Just like my thoughts, they totally distract me from my life and they do pretty much the same thing as my thoughts. They keep me out of God's will and keep me stuck. The funny part is that they are just the next step in a cycle of this Unhealthy Voice. They really are no different from my Unhealthy Voice thoughts because they come after I have a thought about something. So the best way for me to stay focused is for me to remember that feelings aren't facts, and keep walking through them. A book called "Constructive Living" by David K. Reynolds I was given in treatment helped me with this, and I still go back to it.

Here are the Healthy Voice Truths:

God does not judge me.

> *"I have come into the world as light, so that who believes in me should not stay in darkness. If anyone hears my words*

but does not keep them, I do not judge that person. For I did not come to judge the world, but to save the world."
—NIV, John 12:46–47

God never abandons me.

"Keep your lives free from the love of money and be content with what you have, because God has said, "Never will I leave you; never will I forsake you."
—NIV, Hebrews 13:5

My worth rests in the Lord.

The call on my life will be carried through with God if it's His call.

"I can do all things through Christ who strengthens me."
—NIV, Philippians 4:14

I'm never alone even when I feel like I am.

I have to let God heal my heart. I can't do it myself. The timing of healing comes from him as I've learned on the journey so I just have to keep doing the work on my end and trusting Him in the process.

CHAPTER TWENTY:

Addressing my Unhealthy Voice Head On

"Build up your weaknesses until they become your strong points."
—KNUTE ROCKNE

#9: Use your Unhealthy Voice Navigation System to recognize and learn from triggers.

The Vicious Cycle of my Unhealthy Voice

It starts with a thought that is triggered by some internal or external trigger, many of which I laid out above and throughout my story. Often times, it's an environmental, a situational, an emotional trigger, relational, or a physical trigger. Then it makes me feel a certain way. If I chase this feeling, (whether it's physical or emotional) I can head for a dead end. If I respond to it by calling someone to share that feeling or writing it down—I might be able to catch it.

Because of the work I've done, I've learned to stop this sucker in its tracks. It's why we all deserve to find our Healthy Voice because if we don't, we will get continuously stuck in it for life. It is not fun. We beat ourselves up for it. That's why I'm pointing out the cycle here, because I know how long I was stuck in it and how much gentler I am on myself with it today. It goes to show that we aren't crazy when we go to emotionally eat, to get a running or shopping fix, because we can all get stuck in these vicious cycles. We can even get stuck in it when we think we're on a healthy track when we do the same diet over and over again. This thing is the true definition of insanity, doing the same thing over and over again expecting a different result. So we have to stop it in its tracks. We have to practice, practice, practice, and be patient with ourselves while we pull ourselves out of its stormy weather.

Mine gets me when I'm H.A.L.T., as many of us know. I'm hungry, angry, lonely, or tired. It wants to sabotage me when I'm down and make things worse and catches me when I least expect it when I'm at my weakest. There is no right way or one way it approaches us. It's just got its own way with each of us which makes it that much more fun! When I've got a program to treat my physical and mental, and tools to address this cycle—I can confront it instead of look for a temporary fix. Even if it's barking loud or it bites, I can be courageous enough to say, "It was a rough day or week, but I'm learning on this journey." Then I can get accountable instead of beat myself up. It's like the meltdown I had on the way to Nantucket the summer of 2011. It was a tremendous sign of growth within me that I didn't fall apart. I could see in the grand scheme of things that everything was working out together for good and just because we were late, it didn't matter because in God's plan, I got to say goodbye to my Dad.

See, whether they are little baby drama moments or meltdowns moments where we just need to cry and call our best friends, we've just got to be gentle on ourselves and walk through the process instead of choosing our Unhealthy Voice and beating ourselves up –doing something like overeating. It only repeats the cycle, or at least that's what I'm learning as I go.

That's why it's so important for me to know that I'm on a journey in the physical, mental, emotional, and spiritual because I can't do any of it by myself. I've needed guidance from my Higher Power and professionals through it all so that I could find the tools to help me live my life, not just cope with it. Knowing myself helps me navigate these Unhealthy Voice moments without shutting off like I used to and that is an absolute gift. I'm fine with the fact that they come and go sometimes. I just choose not to give into them. The even more beautiful thing is that each one of them reminds me of how much I need God and all the gifts around me in my life to carry me through it.

> *"Let me not pray to be sheltered from dangers, but to be fearless in facing them. Let me not beg for the stilling of my pain, but for the heart to conquer it."*
>
> —*Tago*

A Healthy Voice Timeout

Here's what I do when I get off track with the Unhealthy Voice beast and know it's time for me to meet myself where I'm at:

- I look at what just happened and how my Unhealthy Voice just tried to sabotage me—thought, physical, or emotional feeling, external trigger or memory.
- I am gentle with myself through the whole assessment process.
- I ask myself what's going on physically, mentally, or emotionally at that time.
- I look at what's going on in my day, my life, or my environment that may be adding to the stress
- I look at how I was taking care of myself or not.
- I get present to myself and remember God loves me.
- I remember that I'm getting to know myself better everyday so I don't need to beat myself up anymore.
- I write it down on paper or share it with a Healthy Voice friend. I share what the experience taught me so I know for next time.

- I get reconnected to my truth and my gifts by tuning into my Higher Power and thanking Him for being there to carry me.

The Unhealthy Voice Triggers

"But he said to me, 'My grace is sufficient for you, for my power is made perfect in your weakness.' Therefore I will boast all the more gladly about my weaknesses, so that Christ's power may rest in me."
—*NIV, 2 Corinthians 12:9*

Thoughts, feelings, drama moments, life events out of our control, and then the everyday triggers are the things that we need God for in our life. I will never know all of my triggers, nor know what life brings. I know I will always be surprised by how they come up and what I learn from them. I look forward to the challenges but I also know that the more conscious I am of the Unhealthy Voice games, the more prepared I am for the ways it tries to get me in the small things.

Learning my triggers has been an interesting process, especially now as I am able to give so many of them less power. That certainly doesn't mean they won't be there to try and tempt me at every moment to be distracted. There is no way we can stuff these down or overcome them with sheer will, especially when it comes to food. Alcohol is not an easy substance to navigate in life, but it is something we can live without. Food is not and we need it to live. We also have to live with everything thing the Unhealthy Voice tries that sometimes throws us off track. I've only skimmed the surface in these first few years of recovery. I'm always learning but I have a navigation system down of how they show up so I can call them out and say, "Hey that's a food trigger!"

- *Trigger Substances*—Alcohol and drugs are a no. Sugar in its thousands of forms and flour are my basic no.

- *Food Triggers*—The more I stick to my "go-to foods" the better I'm going to be with these, but I also don't live in a hole. To recognize these triggers, I try to avoid the visual temptation. If I do eat something that triggers me, I recognize how it's affecting my stomach, my mind, or my emotions and make a different choice next time. If it's making me bloated, triggering my blood sugar, or starving me, that's usually a problem. If I'm in the "endless" snacks like anything that comes in a bag with no end to it, that's not good. If I'm eating red meat, it's going to freeze my stomach for a week. If I'm craving it, it's a problem and the sooner I recognize it, the better off I am. I don't read labels for low calories or fat. I read ingredients to keep me out of my trigger stuff and to keep it simple. When I shop I stay out of the aisles that make me think I can have all the stuff that makes me nuts. I highly recommend not touching any food triggers when you are getting started on your Healthy Voice path!

- *Trigger Places*—I can avoid places like fast food restaurants and lots of others that would make it easier to make an Unhealthy Voice choice. I can't always avoid the places that may make the choices available so I come prepared or just make my best choice. The grocery store, convenience stores, rest stops, airports, and Mexican restaurants can all be trigger places!

- *Sensory Triggers*—This one really speaks to them all but sometimes it is overpowering. Knowing when you are triggered by a certain smell or you remember a certain food that tastes, smells, and feels a certain way on your tongue –that just takes you another way that is a major sensory trigger. Knowing where and when you can find these can be a real help to you. That's why finding natural ways to nurture my senses has become so important because they are so much more satisfying than these in the long run. We all know how much a loaf of bread or a batch of cookies freshly baked can throw us off course!

- *Trigger Times*—Being aware of my triggers times helps me to be present to my needs. I have to eat breakfast. Four o'clock is a time I have to eat a snack and evening is a time I have to be present to myself. The same thing goes when the holidays run around, I'm stressed and family plays into the cards. It happens around deadlines, travel times, and just about any time! When I get conscious of them, I can be more prepared the next time I go through those rough times of the day, month, or year.

- *Behavior/Escape Triggers*—My behavior or escape triggers were obviously drinking, smoking, overeating, running, dieting, and spending money. Whatever I can do compulsively is my danger zone. Another big one is moving. I have to stay present in situations that I instinctively want to run from and that is so hard! The more I know when I'm trying to do it and can call it out and get present, the better I feel.

- *Healthy and Thin Ideal Trigger*—This can be a huge trigger for me –especially when I'm trying to just use the tools I've learned while also teaching people not to get caught up in everyone else's idea of healthy. The better I know my Food and Fitness Truth, the less I'm worrying about somebody else's healthy or thin ideal, but it can certainly be a trigger!

- *Trigger Media*—I choose not to read tabloid magazines and I'm selective about what I read in any other magazines or books. I can't watch television shows that cover perfect looking people and their imaginary lives. It makes me nuts because it's not real.

I'd rather not be wasting my time worrying about somebody else's drama. I've got enough of my own but as long as I can recognize it as a trigger, I can choose not to give it power if it's on or just not watch it!

- *People Triggers*—This is one of the biggest triggers around, especially in the age of Facebook. I have to remember that someone else doesn't have it better than me and I especially do not have to compare my life to someone else's or my success. At the same time, if someone triggers me in my home, in my community, in my family, or in the world, I can remember I don't have to control them and leave it at that. The only person I can control is myself and the only choices I can control are my own. There will always be people that judge me people who trigger me. So, it's up to me to find the people who lead me to my Healthy Voice. Some people will come into my life briefly and teach me something. Others will guide me. Others will challenge me. Others will show me the way. Others will just plain old love me. My role is to identify the ones who trigger me and find out what God is teaching me through them or walk away.

- *Trigger Conversations and Situations*—Because life is all about relationships, there will always be conversations and situations that trigger us because no matter how close we are—each of us comes into it with our own history, beliefs, and truths. The same thing goes for situations. What I have to do is walk through them.

- *Travel Triggers*—These are always present whether I'm commuting or on the trip. The key is how I approach the triggers and how prepared I am. It's also in how I adapt when I return from traveling. My truth travels with me if I bring it.

- *Fitness Triggers*—I do not have to beat myself up nor compete with others who are running their own race.

- *Perfect Storm Drama Moments*—These moments will happen. I just have to get over them and walk through them.

- *Emotional Triggers*—These are not fun, but I can recognize that it's okay to feel my feelings and not run away from them.

- *Mental Triggers*—My mind is a dangerous neighborhood and I just need to do the things that help me get out of it.

"No temptation has overtaken you that is not common to man. God is faithful, and he will not let you be tempted beyond your ability, but with the temptation he will also provide the way of escape, that you may be able to endure it."
—NIV, 1 Corinthians 10:13

CHAPTER TWENTY-ONE:

The Tools to Live Your Healthy Voice Journey

#10: Strengthen your Healthy Voice with the Healthy Voice Navigation Tools.

The Lord has given me so many gifts for the journey. I've come to recognize there is a system to it. It's almost a positive system for looking at life. I found that each of these kept coming up in my life so that I could identify them as something like tools for living. I share them with you so you can start to do the same for your journey, to define them in your own way. What is wonderful about them is that they help ground you. They help strengthen you, and make the journey even more rewarding. They are the complement to every step you take. Like a walking stick they provide support. Like a compass, they provide guidance. Like a good friend, they provide companionship. Each one of them is a treasure for you to find around you and within you so that you can keep moving towards the light. They are truly the good stuff of life. They are what take away the power of the food and the triggers, what gets us down. They are what we live for and where we find hope. They will help you stay open to the journey and the people, places, things that show up for you. Even when the road gets rocky, you can find one

The Tools to Live Your Healthy Voice Journey

1. RELY on your faith in your Creator to guide you.
2. EXERCISE your body in a healthy and enjoyable way.
3. NOURISH your body and mind with food that keeps you fueled.
4. DISCOVER the natural world that exists around you.
5. GET CONNECTED with the Healthy Voice Community as it speaks to you.
6. BE AUTHENTIC and ACCOUNTABLE by building relationships with Healthy Voice People in your life who will support you.
7. FIND the Healthy Voice Places that ground you and inspire you.
8. LISTEN FOR Healthy Voice Inspiration through positive music, social media and entertainment.
9. LOOK FOR the Healthy Voice Leaders and Healthy Voice Role Models that can bring out your light.
10. REALIZE the Healthy Voice Spirit is Always with you through every experience, guiding you to your Healthy Voice Purpose.

or more of these to support you. They will keep you in today, with a focus on faith and gratitude. If I know I've got these, I can keep choosing to pick them up every day. I need them to keep me out of my isolation and in accountability with my life. They are the vessel that keeps me tuned into God's voice in my life. In Galatians 5:22-23 it says, *"But the fruit of the Spirit is love, joy, peace, patience, kindness, goodness, faithfulness, gentleness self-control; against such things there is no law."*

1. RELY on your faith in your Creator to guide you.

The First Commandment says to "Love the Lord your God with all your heart and with all your soul and all your mind." I know that I can't rely on my physical or mental strength alone. I need a spiritual strength every day of my life. That's why this is #1. He gives me just one day at a time and it's extremely important for me to remember this on the days when I'm stuck in the past or too far ahead in the future. I'm glad I've got my Higher Power I call God to rely on today. Whatever yours is, that's your path. I hope that in your own way you can rely on that source for everything. My relationship with God is extremely important to me. If I choose to listen for Him and to Him, I will be guided. I know that He is with me through every mountain and valley if I just keep following Him.

"Even though I walk through the darkest valley,
I will fear no evil, for you are with me; your
rod and your staff, they comfort me."
—NIV, Psalm 23:4

When the fear sets in, which it does because I'm human, I have to stay focused on the horizon. With Dad gone, it makes it easier to find solace in this passage below. I find peace in it.

"Set your minds on things that are above, not on things that are on earth, for you have died, and your life is hidden with Christ in God. When Christ in your life is revealed, then you also will be revealed with him in glory."
—NIV, Colossians 3:2-4

Time with God and Prayer

This is a huge part of how I rely on my higher power. I don't think there is a "right" way to do this. We've just got to find our own way that works. When I was growing up, I used to always pray for something. Now when I pray I just thank God and listen for what He is saying out of love and grace through the silence. There is a Catholic hymn that reminds me of this. It reminds me of growing time my Mom and I went through together. It's called "You are Mine".

If you know the Psalm 46 that says, "Be still and know that I am God," you may understand. That time for me comes best when I'm waking up and I can just listen for his voice in the quiet. I can hear Him telling me that He loves me or that he wants me to think about something. I can hear him when I'm praying on my knees or when I'm just driving along in silence. I can hear him when I'm making breakfast and getting ready in the morning just talking to me. I can hear him in the quiet of nature or on a busy street. He is everywhere. That's the best part about Him. Sometimes there are places I go to talk to Him and feel His presence, but sometimes I just have to turn down the radio and listen for Him. Sometimes he blows me away with the most beautiful sunset I could ever imagine. All of these are little conversations with God and most of them barely include a word, just understanding and a prayer to seek and understand His will even when I can't see it. Often times I do read a morning reflection to guide me towards His will and to seek his understanding or I read a passage from the Big Book or the Bible, but either way—I'm seeking His guidance for the day, every day. Without Him, my day is cloudy.

Worship

Worship is a huge part of my time with Him. Sundays are my favorite day of the week because I get to do just that. I don't just get to do this only on Sundays. Worship music is a powerful tool for understanding God's heart. I listen to it all the time and I can just feel His love. It's become a guiding force in my life and always has a message to remind me of the grander picture. It's set on my alarm clock. It's set in my car. I hear it at church on Sundays. I even go to concerts to hear the power of it in person. Whenever I travel I try to find the station for it and often times my playlists for running tune right into it. I hear so many awesome messages of love from it. I truly believe it's created out of God's love and spirit. I can hear God's voice in any music. In fact, it's fun for me to listen for it. I learned from a wonderful man of God at my church named Dr. Bob Laurent that if you listen to any love song it's really about God's love for you, his heart for you. It completely transformed what music I listen to and how I listen to it. Not only that, it helped me understand God more as a loving God rather than a punishing one.

Spiritual Accountability

He's put people in my life that help me stay in tune with the walk I'm taking with Him. I go to church every week not just for the duty of it because I want to worship Him and fellowship with the people of his Kingdom and in the meetings I go to with 12-step. There are so many ways I remain accountable as long as I remain willing to take the journey, I will find that he provides. It's not just a duty. It's the hope and strength that guides me.

2. EXERCISE your body in a healthy and enjoyable way.

We weren't meant to treat our body in the abusive ways that so many of us do. We were meant to treat it with the love it deserves for carrying us. It wants us to exercise, but it doesn't want us to abuse it or think that's the only thing that is worth anything in our lives. Our body knows what it needs if we listen to it, nurture and nourish it. There's a way to strengthen it that helps us rely on it as a tool for living rather than a tool that always need to be fixed, and if we can find it, we can enjoy being in it a lot more. We just have to patient with the journey, rather than looking for the fix all the time. Loving ourselves from the inside out doesn't require always looking perfect on the outside, but the beauty is that it allows us to be fit and vulnerable!

3. NOURISH your body and mind with food that keeps you fueled.

Just like exercise, our bodies want to be nourished with foods that will fuel us for life. They want to be as healthy as possible so we can live long and prosper but our bodies know that there is more to our lives than what we eat. Our bodies want us to keep it simple, not focus all of life on what we put in them. Our bodies also know that food can never satisfy us and it tells us that when we don't get our emotional needs met or when we gain weight from eating too much. Our bodies are telling us to use food as a fuel! They are begging us to put good things in them, not overanalyze what's the "perfect" thing to put in them! The nice thing is, our bodies won't leave us and as we learn to nourish them, they'll thank us.

4. DISCOVER the natural world that exists around you.

"Nothing can cure the soul but the senses, just as nothing can cure the senses but the soul."
—*Oscar Wilde*

How long do we numb our senses and we don't even realize it? How long do we use something like chocolate or candy to replace the hug we need from someone who cares? I was so afraid of being touched that I used the food to replace it for years. It's like my taste buds have expanded beyond the taste itself into a taste for life! Who would have thought that I'd be okay with my body? I used to hate putting on clothes. Now I just love being in comfortable clothes. I don't wear them to cover up my body but because I'm confident in my own skin. Who would have thought I'd be okay with a touch? Now I live for hugs and realize how healing the touch of a hand can be. I love the sensory overload you get from sitting by a fire on a cold night with people you love around you cuddled up to a warm blanket and a pet on your lap. It's amazing what animals can teach you about yourself.

Speaking of touch, massages are something I can appreciate on a whole new level because they release the toxins in my body, heal the physical body, soul and tune me into my senses! I'm so grateful today for being able to appreciate smells! There is nothing better than discovering a new healing scent a candle or lotion that just makes you feel good! So much better than the smell of a cookie or a donut because it's just so natural! It's like my body senses were searching for it all along!

Our senses are something to be discovered, and there is no better place to see how much they can be tuned into than in nature. Start exploring it in real ways and you'll realize that nature is something your senses, mind, and body have probably been missing all along.

5. GET CONNECTED with the Healthy Voice Community as it speaks to you.

Webster defines authentic as "true to one's own personality, spirit, or character." We all have to find those communities where we can be totally ourselves so that we can feel safe as we walk the journey. In reality, we are all the same because we are human. Yet because of the way we've walked our paths, many of us feel that we need support for trials we are going through. All of us really, just need to know that no matter what we are going through—none of us are alone in it. Someone else has gone through it and more importantly, we are loved no matter what. We just have to find the community where we feel that sense of unconditional love so we can become ourselves. The Healthy Voice Community is a community in itself because are all united in our mission to live beyond the weight and beneath the surface. You may need support for an addiction you are recovering from or you may just want to find a yoga community that speaks to your Healthy Voice! You want to be able to walk into places that feel like home and speak to you. I've found them in my community and when I go to other places, I look for those same types of communities so I can feel connected at a soul level. I may not know the people there, but I feel connected to the community. These communities heal us at a soul level if we let them. I find this at my church and in my support community and I am extremely grateful. I also find it on a larger scale in my fitness community and the one I live in today. No matter where you are, you can always find it. This is truly one of the most crucial parts of the process because in order to get out of our Unhealthy Voice selves, we have to hear the stories and connect in community. They aren't just a building. They are places that are full of life where we finally get out of ourselves and realize we are not alone in our struggle. We also realize we don't have to walk it alone. Because of the isolation of my disease, I needed to find those communities to get out of the mental illness that was suffocating my mind and also go deeper in my relationship with Christ by going to church. Online communities are great, but it's that human connection that gives us the courage to look someone in the eye and share our stories. There is tremendous power in community. Here are a few types more detailed.

Healthy Voice Community

You can find us online, in any community, yoga studio, church, college campus or really anywhere.

Our Mission:

We are people that have a story like yours that is our own. We're living life a day at a time beyond the weight and beneath the surface. We're finding our Healthy Voice, living our Healthy Voice, sharing our Healthy Voice and being a Healthy Voice as we go. We will not judge you for your weight. We can't judge ourselves. We love you for your Healthy Voice within you and we are willing to meet you where you are no matter what.

Find us on Social Media, on my website www.findyourhealthyvoice.com and in your town.

A Support Community

As I mentioned earlier, some of us need this. We can't deny ourselves this because it is a crucial piece of the puzzle for many. It doesn't work for everyone, but it has worked for millions. 12-step is the form I took. Because of that community, I have the ability to connect with people anytime, anywhere who struggle with the same thing I do. It is truly a blessing because we can walk the journey together. In fact, the people in the rooms are the ones who have given me these gifts of recovery. They truly taught me this is a "we", not a "me" program. They keep me out of my head and feet on the ground. They know me better than anyone else. There is no way I'd be where I am today without their love and support. They were there the day my Dad died and they are the ones who shared their experience, strength, and hope. They've showed me through living that if I just keep working the program a day at a time, life just keeps getting better. They help me carry the message and remind me who I am so I can become the best of who I was meant to be. It's with them –every week that I can be reminded I have a disease of the mind and an allergy of the body that will catch me and throw me back into the ditch if I'm not humble. It keeps me extremely present to the Unhealthy Voice in my mind and brings some pretty incredible relationships into my life that I'm extremely grateful to have. Not everyone needs one, but it truly can be your greatest gift in life if you are trying to do it all alone.

A Faith Community

This has certainly changed a bit for me. When God wanted me to go deeper into relationship with Him, he wanted me to find the community where I felt comfortable to do that. I found that at Granger Community Church. That is certainly not where everyone will. In fact, your faith journey is absolutely and unequivocally your own. Everything I've shared about my faith journey in this book is my experience just as this faith community I've found is what works for me today. Its mission speaks right to my heart, "Helping people take their next steps towards Christ . . . together." From my recovery, to my faith walk, to my career—it folds into all of it. Not only that, the sense of community I feel is overwhelming and the people I've met who are so willing to share authentically astounds me. What's even cooler is that it isn't just one church in my community. We're connected to tons of churches all over the country with amazing Pastors leading them. None of them are the same. They've all got their own style. I love visiting their websites, or going to visit them when I travel. It's pretty cool to feel like you are part of a network of people who are all on the same mission. The best part about it, much like the support community, is that you can always find someone who's been where you've been or someone to serve that needs to know where you've been. We all walk the journey together and it's a beautiful thing.

Health and Wellness Community

The community around health and wellness is so advanced right now that it's not hard to find. The tricky part for me has been finding the places that really tune into my Healthy Voice since the main focus is so much on the physical. When I work out, I try to focus on getting out of my mind by getting into my body and connecting to the Healthy Voice Spirit within me. As someone who is triggered by excessive talk about the body, diets, and working out—it can be truly triggering for me sometimes to find a community that speaks to my focus beneath the surface. I can also accept that's what people are looking for! It may be what has kept me so balanced in my recovery from my exercise addiction as well. So I try to find those places that closely match my Healthy Voice. If I can't find one, I look for the Healthy Voice Leaders in those communities who help me tune into my Healthy Voice with their presence or even their music. Then I look for the Healthy Voice People in those communities that seem to have a gentler approach to it that I seem to gravitate towards. If you find people that have the same fitness goals as you in this community it can be pretty awesome when you find you know them from other communities! I've found that running, cycling indoor and outdoor, and yoga were all communities where I could find people that really matched my Healthy Voice. Their love of those sports often times showed me their love of the journey. If it became only about the sport, then I knew they wouldn't want what I had. I can be the Healthy Voice in these communities as well. In fact, I love when I meet yoga or spin instructors who are being a Healthy Voice through their teaching, and then their message! It's powerful stuff. I love when someone calls to tell me they went to a fitness class or met someone that had the Healthy Voice aura about them. It gets me so excited because that means two people are sharing the light! I'll get a voice mail or a text of someone sharing how they found their Healthy Voice, "Hey Mere, I was a new yoga studio and it was Healthy Voice. I met a spin instructor who was totally Healthy Voice." What they are finding is their Healthy Voice and sharing it! Love it!

6. BE AUTHENTIC and ACCOUNTABLE by building relationships with Healthy Voice People in your life who will support you.

"To be fully seen by somebody, then, and be loved anyhow—this is a human offering that can border on miraculous."
—Elizabeth Gilbert

To be authentic means being honest, open and who you are with another person. It's hard stuff. Yet, that's what the Healthy Voice Journey is all about. That's why we go to these communities and find our Healthy Voice, so we can share the journey with people who can walk alongside us. Because of these people, I know that I don't have to walk alone ever again. It's in these people, I've found stories I never expected to relate to and have hope in people who've overcome something I never imagined I could. I don't know where I'd be without these people in my life. Each one of them has been a gift. They haven't been checks I've marked off a box. They've just been gifts that have come into my life at the perfect time. Some of them have been with me and carried me through my recovery. Others are sharing how they've gotten through the grieving process, while others are sharing how their faith in God got them through the toughest times. I'm amazed at the power of our stories to overcome our struggles. For it's not in our results that we find the companionship but in sharing our struggles.

"Success is not measured by what you accomplish, but by the opposition you have encountered, and the courage with which you have maintained the struggle against overwhelming odds."
—Orison Swett Marden

I have found this concept of sharing a common struggle and being able to connect with them is incredibly uplifting. Obviously

12-step showed me how true this has been. I find connection with people who come into those rooms I'd never expect. I find I can be accountable on a deeper level with a sponsor. I find it with my dearest friend in the program who walks with me. She's like a spiritual sister. I find it with friends I've met at church who have walked a similar journey. One is a writer and friend who to me, is a like a guide, a spiritual mentor and connector. These people get me, and allow me to meet myself where I am. Yet, it doesn't stop there. There are people I shared the experience of the White House and September 11th with who are special to me. There are people I went to Notre Dame with and people I grew up with back in Philadelphia. There is my family, my Mom and my Dad who've been through everything with me. My Grandma Cass was a huge Healthy Voice for me when I was growing up and is hanging out with Dad up in heaven. All along the journey, I have always been guided. I've always had that Healthy Voice person in my life watching out for me. It's just now I get to intentionally choose them and make them a positive part of my life! I've found that these Healthy Voice People become a rock through every storm. They are the true friends I can call that I couldn't call when food was the main thing in my life. No matter what I'm going through, I seek out the spiritual guides, mentors, or companions to guide me through it as I turn to God for spiritual strength. I learned this more than ever when my Dad died. The people who showed up are the people that always answer the phone. Contrary to popular belief, it isn't some perfect looking clique of friends. It's just a few really amazing friends near and far, some family that show up. Period. You know who you are. Thank you. You have made me a stronger woman and person for being there when I needed you.

"Then the Lord God said, "It is not good that the man should be alone; I will make him a helper fit for him."
—NIV, Genesis 2:18

Having relationships to navigate the journey of life makes it all worth it. Expecting people to be superhuman is what takes away the beauty. I've learned and I'm continuing to learn every day that they are all a process, and if we just keep going through the changes, we'll get through just fine. I know when I'm frustrated with someone else it's usually something going on with me. Just like the food, relationships are the substance of life but I can't suck them dry. People are people. I've learned also that no matter what happens in a relationship, if I'm disappointed it's usually God's way of asking me to go deeper into reliance on Him. "People are in our life for a reason, a season or a lifetime." This saying helps me find peace as I navigate my relationships and try to turn them over to God. We can trust him!

"And we know that in all things God works
for the good of those who love him, who have
been called according to his purpose."
—NIV, Romans 8:28

Dating and Love Relationships

"Being deeply loved by someone gives you strength,
while loving someone deeply gives you courage."
—Lao Tzu

This is a whole other topic for another book in the future but if you are trying to navigate this, I would say try to listen to your Healthy Voice here as well. Much like the food, the guy/or girl you are dating, you like, or are married to cannot be everything to you so put down the hammer and let Him be the guy He can be for you! Stop looking for perfection and find the guy who meets you where you are so you can meet Him where He is. It's about walking with someone on the journey, not looking for him to "complete" you, or finding one that looks like he should be on "The Bachelor." That's just as bad as trying to get the perfect body. So, simmer down and fall in love with yourself before you go trying to find your Healthy Voice in some guy. He'll complement you, but even if he says you are a beautiful a million times or becomes a millionaire, he won't satisfy you in the way that only God can with His love. So don't put that pressure on some poor guy (or girl, whatever!) Believe me, you'll be much happier with a guy who is there for you rather than find in your TV fantasy or resume!

7. FIND the Healthy Voice Places that tune you into your Healthy Voice.

I've had to change the places I go in recovery. Many of us do. When you think of it, you can first think of the places you go socially or even where you go for work. But they can be anything from your home, to the restaurant you frequent to, to your doctor's office, to your gym. You've got to be really intentional about choosing the places now that speak to your Healthy Voice. You aren't going to get them all at once, but you can certainly pay attention to the places that aren't a Healthy Voice for you and maybe work to create a Healthy Voice space in them, or find a place to replace them. It's hard work finding those places that speak to your Healthy Voice but when you do it's like a breath of fresh air. Why? Because you feel connected to your Healthy Voice Spirit. You often find not just a place but, a Healthy Voice community, people who are leading you and people who are walking alongside you. You find a Healthy Voice atmosphere that just makes you say "This is a Healthy Voice Place for me."

Home

Of course they say home is where the heart is and it is true. It has taken me forever to get comfortable in my home, but I've realized it's just me getting even more comfortable with myself. Sometimes I find myself adjusting things in my environment or getting things more in order and I realize it's just my Healthy Voice reflecting in my environment helping me to get life even more in order. It's all part of the process and I get excited about making my home a Healthy Voice especially since it used to be such an Unhealthy Voice where I isolated. Our home is a reflection of the love we have for ourselves and we should take the time to nurture it and take care of it.

My Town and Others

We've all got the places that are familiar to us in our community. We've got our grocery store, our dry cleaners, our coffee shop, and our restaurants. We've got our gym, our yoga studio, our doctor's office, our chiropractor's office and our favorite shops to get gifts for people. I love going to those places because I find people in those places that connect to my soul. It's connecting with people I know and don't know that brings me peace. I love living in a fairly small town because I can see two people every week at the grocery store that just warm my heart and it's great! I can go to a yoga class with my favorite yoga teacher, Roxie, who brings me peace. I can go anywhere and pretty much find connection with other people and feel more connected to my Healthy Voice in those places in my home community.

When I go into these places, wherever they are, I know that I'm going to get the services I need, the information and friendly atmosphere that I'm looking for in self-care. We don't take this into account half the time but it has an impact. It has an impact just as much as the people around us, or leading us with their voice to make our bodies the ultimate thing in our lives. It's up to us to walk into these communities with a Healthy Voice perspective so we don't get thrown off.

I love where I live, so where you live can be a Healthy Voice Place for you. I love the Midwest. It screams America, the simple life, natural beauty, and real people. Everything about it speaks non-judgment. There are so many beautiful places in Northern Michigan. The Midwest just has a lot of beauty—inside and out—to share. It gets a bad rap because everyone thinks it's just cornfields but there is no mistake that I'm living smack dab in the middle of the country! The Midwest is the best! I love traveling to other communities too, big ones and small ones—- I love finding the Healthy Voice Places within those communities. It's like one big discovery mission of the Healthy Voice. You can judge a place by its surface but it's about what it offers to help guide people to their Healthy Voice. There are towns that are a total Healthy Voice already—like Austin, Texas—with everything they have to offer. I love finding out about the 5ks that are in town bringing the community together, going to the best coffee shop, finding a yoga studio, finding a trail or a great gift shop. Then there are towns that have the power within to be it. They just need the knowledge and resources to tap it. There are tons of them in the Midwest and I'm all about inspiring them! I just love discovering it wherever I go. It makes life so much more fun to find your Healthy Voice wherever you go.

The Natural Landscape

"We need to find God, and he cannot be found in noise and restlessness. God is the friend of silence. See how nature—trees, flowers, grass-grows in silence; see the stars, the moon and the sun, how they move in silence . . . We need silence to be able to touch souls."

—Mother Theresa

Nature is my ultimate Healthy Voice Place. As soon as I set my eyes on it in any way, I feel peace and communion with my higher power. It has taught me patience during change and that the world around me is bigger than me. It teaches me that in the grand scheme of things we are all one. It doesn't matter what I'm doing in nature but when I'm in communion with it, I feel alive and closer to heaven. I love to be on a mountain hike, a walk on the beach, or just driving by it on the road. I love taking my yoga mat outside. I love to watch the grandeur of a long, slow sunset on Lake Michigan. It's like having a long talk with Dad or soaking in that unconditional love from above. When I really need to be grounded, nature is where I go to talk with Dad and God. I've got a few places I go to do that but I often find I get surprised by a random sunset, a sky full of glimmering sunrays or a little butterfly shooting by me.

The places where nature shows its greatest beauty blows me away. I'm so glad my Mom introduced me to the Grand Canyon in college that I've gotten to experience Montana and so many other places. But I'm not done yet. I've got more nature in me! Mike and I dream of getting a pass to all the National Parks just so we can see them all, and taking the kids on hiking adventures. We try to take it in as much as possible in our everyday life, by taking runs outside and going for bike rides. We love sharing the power of nature together. I love helping others notice it because nature is where I believe you truly find your Healthy Voice. Yes, I do see retreats in the future in very beautiful places!

My Special Healthy Voice Places

We've all got our special Healthy Voice Places. Mine have been pretty obvious here. But it's important to find yours. Every one of mine connects me somehow to my Healthy Voice Spirit in some way, and I'm grateful for each when I arrive. Whether it's Leland, Michigan, Notre Dame Campus on a football Saturday, or running around Town Lake in Austin, Texas—we've all got those places that speak to us. Go out and explore yours!

8. LISTEN FOR Healthy Voice Inspiration through music, social media and entertainment.

We all live in a society that is technologically overloaded. It cannot only be exhausting to keep up with the trends, but it can be draining. We don't even recognize how loud the Unhealthy Voice can speak to us in these areas if we aren't careful. The one that tells us it's all about having the right body, the right guy, the right things, the right life and that everyone else has it, but we don't? Yes, that's the one I'm talking about. That's why I want you to intentionally start listening for your Healthy Voice in these areas and in turn, being a Healthy Voice for those around you.

Music

I certainly don't expect everyone to listen to worship music like I do. Music taste is as personal as food tastes. I will tell you that's not all I listen to. Yet everything I do listen to is intentional. It's got lyrics that inspire me and don't bring me down. They usually move me on the bike or the run. They move me emotionally, or they get me pumped. I've always been a lyrics and music person so they've both got to be powerful for me. I am always looking for songs to add to one of my Healthy Voice playlists. I've got workout mixes that I use for riding, spinning, and running that put me in the rhythm of my Healthy Voice. Often times they've got lyrics that inspire me and sometimes they are just film scores. When it comes to yoga, I generally like it quiet but, I also like it with music that's going to reach me on a rhythmic and emotional level. Other times I'm going for a long drive and I want to have a great playlist so I make one. When my Dad passed, I made a couple of our old favorites. I sent them out to family, which is something I've done ever since I was a kid for people I love. I know it's cheesy and old school but making playlists is a form of therapy for me—whether it's to workout, grieve or drive. Music to me is the language of the spirit and it always gives me the perspective if I need if I'm choosing it wisely. You aren't going to find me listening to a depressing love song that makes me think I'm a victim! Those days are gone! So whether you are going on Youtube to find a video, Spotify, Itunes or wherever—make a Healthy choice on there! Fill your mind with the good, positive inspiring stuff that motivates you for the journey!

Social Media

This can be the most unhealthy voice place in the world and it can be where you can be the most Healthy Voice in your social network circle. Go to the website to find out navigation.

Okay, this can also be one of the absolute unhealthiest places for our Unhealthy Voice. If you want to hear your Healthy Voice, you have GOT to be intentional about the people you choose to follow and what you post. Also, spending time on these can be a real killer, so don't let them do it to you.

Facebook™—It's a great way to keep up with everyone you know, see photos of people's trips or promote your business. We all know how it can get negative. If you are following someone who is a literal train wreck—click hide. It's that simple. If you are following someone who you find yourself gossiping about or trying to compete with, you may need to do the same. Intentionally choose to follow those people and organizations that are a positive influence in your life. Period. If other people get catty, don't participate. I don't care if you are in college or you are in your forties. Dropping and adding friends is childish. If you find yourself comparing, get off the thing and do something positive! If you find yourself comparing to one person in particular, question your thoughts and do something about it. Ultimately, I'm choosing to follow positive people that inform me or inspire me.

Twitter™—Follow the people who inspire you or maybe bring a laugh to your day. If you want a Healthy Voice it doesn't really help to follow every single quick-fix tweeter out there. I can find some great articles from the experts or organizations that have information that helps me guide others to their Healthy Voice. Yet, I have to follow the same policy on Twitter as I do on Facebook—positive people that inform me or inspire me. If I were following a bunch of people focused on fixing their bodies, I'd probably be thinking I needed to do that. Instead I follow inspirational leaders, family, and friends and new sites. Yes, we all like train wrecks but it is toxic.

Pinterest™—Who doesn't love it? Use it in a positive way. I go on to decompress after a stressful day. My favorite pages are the quotes, the wedding and the home furnishings. Be careful about what you find on the fitness page and the Entertainment one—both can be a bit Unhealthy Voice telling you it's all about the fix, being skinny, losing the weight. I'm going to have some Healthy Voice images up on my site so go check it out and create your own! Let's start a Healthy Voice campaign on Pinterest!

Go to my website *www.findyourhealthyvoice.com* to find out more about the hashtag system.

Entertainment

When it comes to television, I'll watch anything that is entertaining. I realize like music taste, this is relative for everyone. I've found that television can be a waste of time and pretty toxic though. Reality shows (not all of them), gossip, and any show that is just totally fabricated fantasy can be out of the question—especially if it's teaching young girls unhealthy habits! Those teen shows aren't like they were when original 90210 was around! I'll watch educational, documentary, or home improvement shows. I really love the shows that are inspirational and share about people's victory over something. That's someone sharing a Healthy Voice with the world. If I see this kind of thing happening in a movie, I'm even more inspired. I love movies that talk about the journey or how you can live a more inspired life (which seem to be few and far between). I love the movie the Way with the Sheens, The Shift with Wayne Dyer, Way of the Peaceful Warrior, Secretariat, and The

Blindside. I steer away from the fantasy ones but love the romantic comedy here and there. Yet, I have to walk into it knowing that it's not real! I watch for the news but I can't focus on it because it brings me down. I can pray for those suffering and be present to those suffering in my own life, to find where God calls me. I also think of online movies. YouTube is so big these days that you can find just about anything. I choose not to watch most of the stuff that is not healthy for me. I do love to watch inspiring videos, advertisements, and music videos because I love to see what moved people to create the video behind their lyrics and sound. I can listen to radio that is educational or inspiring. I love tuning into Joyce Meyer in the morning and Dave Ramsey in the afternoons. I go nuts when I tune into here people arguing about politics! I know how much my Dad loved it, and it makes me think of him, but it's just not my thing.

Be mindful of the "Apps" you choose for your computer, mobile device or Facebook! They can be absolute time suckers when you've already got a time sucker on your hands! If you are reading books or magazines, make your own choices but give power to the stuff that informs you, not the stuff that strengthens your Unhealthy Voice and continuously makes you think there is a fix. If you can come at it knowing that it's knowledge for the journey maybe in the physical, that's great—but don't get thrown back into the fix journey!

Go to entertainment events and concerts that lift your spirit too! Everything you do to entertain you, make it intentional! Check out our website for some navigation on these too.

9. LOOK FOR Healthy Voice Leaders and Role Models that can bring out your light.

We have all been led to our Healthy Voice by people, whether they touch us in our immediate life, or they'll never get to meet us because they touch so many. Some of them have helped us make important decision and choices that have guided us to where we are today. Others have become what I call Healthy Voice Role Models in our lives. Either way, they have touched us. We may not even know it yet in many cases. The important thing is to look for those Healthy Voice Leaders to guide us and also to find those people who can be Healthy Voice Role Models for us in whatever way we may need it. All of those people are gifts for us on the journey to guide us along the way. Check out our website and social media to find out more about the ones we're finding to inspire you!

There are so many Healthy Voice Leaders who have inspired me I can't even count them here. One is a music artist, Bono. One leads people to Financial Peace, Dave Ramsey. One leads women to a deeper faith, Christine Caine. One is my Mom. If she hadn't raised me, I wouldn't be where I am today. She showed me with strength, courage, and determination that I could do whatever I wanted to do and get through it all with faith in God. She taught me to never, ever give up and I'm forever grateful for that. One is my Dad. If he hadn't been a leader in his own passionate career and his family, I wouldn't be where I am today. I am incredibly grateful for his passion, his unwavering love and commitment, and his belief in me. I'll miss him like all get out forever, but I know he's with me every second inspiring me with his spirit. He's a pretty powerful angel up there and I feel like a lucky girl down here.

There are so many people in my life and the world that inspire me. They've got stories, and when they share them I am blown away. I just love seeing their light shine from the inside out. I can't wait to meet more of you!

10. REALIZE that the Healthy Voice Spirit is always with you through every experience, guiding you to your Healthy Voice Purpose.

When you start to recognize the light of the Healthy Voice all around you, and in people—you realize that if you can see it in them, it's in you. It reminds me of a song that I love by a guy who to me is a total

Healthy Voice as he uses his gifts and shares his story to inspire those he reaches with his music. His name is Brandon Heath. I saw him sing at a State Fair in Indiana and heard him share his story and his amazing voice. His song, "The Light in Me" plays in my head as I write this. Check out the video and more on his website www.brandonheath.net.

Knowing we have that light in us reminds us that it's a spirit that is always within us, guiding us through every single experience we go through. I've shared with you my victories and my struggles. This music artist is authentic because he does the same. By finding hope in our struggles and the light within us, we can be led to that purpose we've got within us. That purpose may just be a light for someone else. It doesn't mean we have to save the world or be famous. It could just be smiling at someone walking down the street today that needed it. We just have to realize that even if we may not see it, someone else may see that light in us and because of that, we can be that light for someone who may need it just as we do.

> *"Our deepest fear is not that we are inadequate. Our deepest fear is that we are powerful beyond measure. It is our light, not our darkness that most frightens us. We ask ourselves, 'Who am I to be brilliant, gorgeous, talented, fabulous?' Actually, who are you not to be? You are a child of God. Your playing small does not serve the world. There is nothing enlightened about shrinking so that other people won't feel insecure around you. We are all meant to shine, as children do. We were born to make manifest the glory of God that is within us. It's not just in some of us; it's in everyone. And as we let our own light shine, we unconsciously give other people permission to do the same. As we are liberated from our own fear, our presence automatically liberates others."*
>
> —Marianne Williamson

We think our life purpose has to be so big, and if it isn't—it's so small. We often tie purpose to career, thinking that if we aren't good at one thing we must not be good at anything. Sometimes we think that if someone told us it's not a good enough job, that we can't be successful at it, but if it truly speaks to our spiritual gifts, it could very well be part of our purpose. I'm always amazed when I'm talking with someone who seems lost in this part of the journey. Yet, then I hear their struggle and how they've overcome it. I know this can be touchy, feely for some. I also know it doesn't mean everyone will make a career out of it, but I do know that when we serve others or share our stories with those who may just be getting started on a similar journey—we can often find what this journey is all about.

"The search for the purpose of life has puzzled people for thousands of years. That's because we typically begin at the wrong starting point—ourselves. We ask self-centered questions like 'What do I want to be? What should I do with my life? What are my goals, my ambitions, my dreams for my future?' But focusing on ourselves will never reveal our life's purpose."
—*Rick Warren*

We have to remember that spirit within us will show us the way to ours and that through everything there is a purpose. Through every season of trial, every mountain and every valley, if we find the good and trust God, we'll find the way he's planned that is far greater than anything we had planned. We'll find that he's with us through it all, even when we can't see it and we want it to be there so badly. He's there.

CHAPTER TWENTY-TWO:

Continue your Journey by Sharing your Healthy Voice

#11: Be willing to share the power of your Healthy Voice Story so that it may help others.

"Other people are going to find healing in your wounds. Your greatest life messages and your most effective ministry will come out of your deepest hurts."
—RICK WARREN

This book wasn't written just for you. It was written for the people you are going to share it with in your life. I'm not talking about just sharing it with friends or in your book club. I'm talking about getting into action with it. I'm talking about sharing what it's taught you or what you've learned about yourself in the process. I want you to share with those people how you started to find your Healthy Voice because of it. It's really to help those who need to get free from their Unhealthy Voice. There are too many people stuck in chains in some way shape or form and they need to hear your Healthy Voice. They need your story of hope. Then they need you to hand them the book so they can take the journey themselves and hand it to someone else who can learn to get on their own path. Everyone who wants to get beyond the weight and look at what else might be going on deserves to do just that. Being able to share your story makes that relationship connection begin from the very start. It's more than just a book. It's someone saying, "Hey, I read this book. I found my Healthy Voice. I know you can find yours." It's brings a community to this issue of weight that is desperately needed. It's not just for the food addiction but for everyone who struggles with an Unhealthy Voice in their minds or bodies. It takes the "this is my body and I have to fix it" aspect away from the whole thing. It shows that together we can walk no matter what.

What is your Healthy Voice Story?

Think about the traditional ways that motivate you to "get healthy." It's the before and after photos right? That is awesome! Yet there is more to the story and that is nothing to be ashamed of because that's the good stuff! I absolutely love how motivated people become to get physically healthy and how often it changes their lives. Yet, this is different. Sharing your Healthy Voice Story means sharing how you got there, what was happening, what program you chose to change you, how the Healthy Voice helped you, and what parts of it are helping to carry you. Sharing honestly about your triggers would be amazing. This is all about being authentic—not focusing on the physical results alone, but how you feel about your whole self. I want you to go as deep as you are willing to go to inspire them to change as well.

When I see someone else's light, it's like we're sharing our truth. I feel at peace. It's not something we share just because we have accomplished something. It is something we share because we are both human and real, not just robotic physical beings trying to get better bodies. So boring! I want to hear what inspires you, motivates you, and what puts that light in you! I want to hear who inspires you and who are the role models (beyond the weight) that keep you going!

I want to share a few stories of just a few people I've met who found their Healthy Voice light in their own way by taking that first step to their Healthy Voice through this physical transformation. They are on their own journey of course, but I interviewed them because I could see the Healthy Voice light in them. It's not a journey about how much weight you lost, what the scale says or your measurements. It's about what you've learned about yourself and how you've grown on the inside! Each one of these people had their own issues with their Unhealthy Voice and found they had to make the necessary changes to adapt, but they are all learning to live with their own version of their Healthy Voice!

Lisa

I met Lisa Neese in 2011 the first time I was the behavior modification coach for the American Heart Association (AHA) Better U Program where a group of women participated to lose weight and prevent heart disease. Lisa and I met one on one to talk about her Healthy Voice and what in her environment could set her back from staying on track with the 6-week program. After that, we'd do conference calls to discuss triggers and the like to stay on top of it. One year later, I went back to be the coach for the program again and saw that my friend Lisa was the guest speaker for the kick-off event looking like a completely different person! She had been able to maintain 105-pound weight-loss. Her confidence was up and she looked great! Of course, I saw her for what was shining from the inside out—an inner confidence that I knew came from the journey not just the number. So I asked to introduce her to the new group of women. When I did, I asked the women to try not to listen to the number she shares but what motivated her to start, how she did it and how she continues to do it now, because that is where her victory lies. That's where I wanted the newcomers to find the hope, because I know that's where I get my hope! She shared her story again at the luncheon and stood in a crowd of a couple hundred. Then I shared the book with her and she realized that she did have a Healthy Voice that she never realized. She said in her email response,

"I didn't realize it at the time but I do have a healthy voice. I have leaned on God to help me as well. If you remember I said before I started my journey I did a lot of meditating about what I was going to need to succeed to gain control over my health. It was then that I realized that it wasn't in my control. I knew I was going to need strength, drive, motivation, and determination to make this a successful journey, or a life change. I also knew I could not cultivate these things on demand. How do you suddenly get the motivation you need to go to the gym after work when you really don't want to? I have learned that these tools I needed are gifts from God, and I can (and still do) call upon Him when I'm in need. I agree with you that we all need someone higher and for me that is God. I've learned that I'm just a weak, vessel and need God at the helm."

How amazing is that? I truly believe that because she grounded herself in that physical program and felt that accomplishment she was able to feel the power of God's strength in her life during that time.

Cindy

These next two people don't know each other but what they have in common is that they both came to a point where some type of stomach surgery was the option in finding their Healthy Voice through making a physical change first. What I find amazing about both of them is their willingness to share their Healthy Voice Story and in so doing show to others who may be looking to something like surgery for the fix, that it's more than just a fix. What I've learned from them is what I've learned from my own path. Life doesn't start or stop when you get the surgery. It keeps going. Everything isn't all figured out. You've still go to learn how to live life on life's terms and deal with the internal struggles you have with food that a physical surgery just can't do. Theirs was some kind of surgery. Mine was treatment. It doesn't matter what it is that gets us physically grounded, whether it's losing the weight or getting out of our heads with it—we still have to learn to modify our behaviors and adapt to life with it. I admire their courage for sticking it out and realizing that they don't have to give up because the surgery didn't fix it. They keep walking. They are both a tremendous Healthy Voice in my mind.

I met Cindy at one of my workshops when I first started coaching.

When Cindy started to look back where it all began, it became clear to her how long she had struggled. "I am taken back to moments as a child of stealing cookies out of the freezer which were supposed to be for a special occasion. I also took seconds and thirds at dinner and I ate fast for fear the food would run out."

Then, once Cindy had her own spending money, she turned to the delicacy of sweet treats and fast food. She watched for food and she watched for her weight, as early as the 4th grade. She remembers her weigh-in at the doctors.

"My first obsession with my weight was when my fourth grade report card reflected, 'Weight: 90 lbs.' I don't even know if that is normal or not," says Cindy. But it brought it to her attention.

"As I look back at photos, I was not a fat child. I was just not petite. I felt so fat. I believe it was the picture of myself in my head that made it my reality. I weighed in at 260 pounds in 2002.

Not surprisingly, Cindy's relationship with food did not change as she got older and she looked for a new solution.

"I was recently divorced and drowning in the situation with my weight. I began to consider gastric bypass as a solution for me."

Cindy was fighting hard for the solution she believed would fix it all.

"I challenged my insurance company and won. I dreamed of the day I would no longer be the largest person in a room. I wondered what my mind would be full of when I didn't have to measure myself to others in that way anymore."

Cindy knew the risks of the surgery but it did not matter.

"I was so depressed that the reality of a possible death in surgery did not distract me. The night before my surgery I wrote a good-bye letter to my two daughters, then ages 13 and 15."

As many others who choose gastric bypass as a solution, Cindy started seeing results. The weight, as anticipated, fell off at a good speed and six months after surgery she found her self 100 pounds smaller.

According to Cindy, "Life was good. Never again was I going to have to worry about my weight."

Wrong.

"Though I continue to do well, playing with sugar has enabled my system to accept it and I could eat myself clear through the surgery if I desire. I don't desire!"

"I have been working with a wellness coach for the last three years. What I am learning through her is that my behavior change is futile unless I learn to love myself. That is what I am working on. I am reshaping the voices in my head."

Cindy realized the gastric bypass surgery was a step forward but not an overall solution.

"I am learning to love myself no matter what size or shape I am. I wish I would have done this work earlier, and then I would not have been disappointed in what my body looked like after the weight loss. I would be able to appreciate my body for what it was and what it today. I cannot do that without being in tune to my healthy voice. My gastric bypass surgery was not the solution. My Healthy Voice ™ is."

What I love about Cindy is that she's recently become a Life Coach. She tunes into the creative side of her Healthy Voice by designing picture collages for people, and she wants to help those who have struggled like she has with their own Unhealthy Voice after surgery.

Umberto

I met Umberto Fedeli at a luncheon during the Cleveland Clinic Obesity Conference in 2011 when I was consulting with them for the Curves project. I was amazed to hear this Healthy Voice Story. This man was just like me! As he sat next to his surgeon and shared how the surgery helped him, he shared honestly about how he still needed to work with his food issues every single day. Here was a gentleman sharing how the surgery saved his life but was not the answer to all his problems. "More people need to hear his story!" I thought. Thankfully he was willing to let me interview him for the book.

As he struggled with weight over the years, Fedeli read hundreds of books on the subject, tried every diet and had a personal trainer for 14 years. Ultimately, he decided on bariatric surgery at the Cleveland Clinic. But the journey did not stop there.

"Surgery isn't enough. I've got the same brain," said Fedeli.

After the surgery, "People said you've got to be happy!" I replied, "Not really. I still have the problem! I love candy, I love sweets. I still have all the bad habits."

"The only thing that has changed since I had my stomach reduced is I am able to eat less and in turn get full faster. The surgery has been a management tool. It is not a solution. All the challenges I had have not changed."

During the interview he told me how he was sharing his Healthy Voice because he knew carrying the message helped him stay with it. He shared with me how he has made it his life's mission to try and help as many people as he can who also struggle with obesity.

"When they share these challenges, the more it reminds me of my own challenges and the more it reminds me of what I need to do. It is a constant reinforcement, a lifelong process," says Fedeli.

"I wish I could say I have solved all the issues. I can say I do manage them better now. I still eat things I like. I still pick at food. I just don't do them to the volume or the degree. It is an ongoing process."

Fedeli learned some amazing lessons on his journey to finding his own Healthy Voice. "If you have this challenge, it's going to be a lifelong challenge. You have to have a commitment for exercise. It helps to keep you in better condition to be more cognizant and help you make better choices. I understand now it is all about progress, not about perfection. I am the same person with all of the struggles."[11]

Our Healthy Voice Stories Together

If you see your story in mine, or in any of these few stories then you've got it in you to share yours too. I'm not saying you have to share it publicly, but if you share your walk with someone and share your Healthy Voice with someone who needs it, it can strengthen you for the journey. I learned in 12-step recovery that carrying the message is one of the key steps to staying with the program. It's something I carry over to this work.

So I encourage you to share it if the opportunity to presents itself. If someone is having trouble getting motivated to start—share where you were and what motivated you to start. If someone is struggling with sticking with it—share with them, how you find the strength to endure within. Share the tools of your Healthy Voice. Go get coffee with them or go for a workout! If you need someone to walk with you because you feel alone, find someone you feel comfortable with sharing your whole story and you will be more confidence in sharing it authentically.

If you are thinking you don't have it in you, I can tell you that you do. You've got it in you to start somewhere. You've got it in you to take that step forward and share with someone some aspect of how your Healthy Voice has helped you through physical, mental, emotional or spiritual transformation. When you recognize it, you've got the first step up the staircase. Believe me, if you've been through anything big in your life and you are still here, you've had it. If you've had a physical transformation with a weight-loss program, you've tapped into it. If you've found a relationship with God, you've found it. Now you've just got to give yourself some credit for how far you've come, see where you can take your next step, find who you want to share your journey with and look for that person who needs you to share your Healthy Voice with them. If you can't get motivated, think about where you are struggling and think about what kind of story might make you motivated and pray for it to come into your life. I know when I'm going through rough days with my grief, I make a call to someone who has been through it or I sit down and get quiet.

Above ALL else, it is okay to share this journey. This no longer has to be an "I'm in this all alone" thing. You may be in your body but you are not meant to keep this journey to yourself. God's with you even! If you are willing to look beyond the fix, you are ready to get to your story. Then you are ready to share your story. Come on, let's go! You know I didn't share my story to just write it! I shared it so you could find the courage to share yours with someone who needs to hear yours!

So get ready to share the good stuff beyond the results and the way you look because that's where the miracles happen—when we share our struggles. We've all been through something and there is someone who needs to hear how we got through it. It's how we got through that something which will give us the strength to get through where we're going next.

"Your journey has molded you for your greater good, and it was exactly what it needed to be. Don't think you've lost time. There is no shortcutting to life. It took each and every situation you have encountered to bring you to the now. And now is right on time."

—*Asha Tyson*

CHAPTER TWENTY-THREE:

Be a Healthy Voice

#12: Be the Healthy Voice Light for your self, for another—for the world.

"Be the change you wish you see in the world."
—GANDHI

Whether you realize it or not, you are being a Healthy Voice right now in some way. You are present to someone or something in your life. Maybe it's your family, your kids, your college, or high school career, your aging parent, your employees, or your work. I want you to think right now about how you are BEING present. What are the gifts that you have in your life? Do you have a family you love, a roof over your head, a paying job, a next meal to eat? If you have things to be grateful for, then you've got a Healthy Voice! I know I do and I need to remember it on those days it's hard to BE that Healthy Voice.

So the key is not in just being physically present or emotionally present. The key is being as fully present as you can be, showing up for your life with your feet on the ground. I'm talking about not stuck in the past, not living in the future, or wandering into fantasy. I'm talking about not worrying about someone else's business but your own. I'm talking about showing up for yourself. The question is how are you going to BE a Healthy Voice today, tomorrow, next week and in your life. Really, how are you going to BE it? How are you going to BE the best you can be on the inside and out so can really embrace everything life has to offer?

I'm not talking about tapping into your perfectionism thinking you have to do this whole thing perfect now. I'm talking about digging deep into that potential you've got to really be the best person you can be for every cell in your body and every person you touch in your life. How deep are you willing to go? How strong are you willing to make your Healthy Voice? How much are you willing to rely on the power greater than you that wants you to BE who you were truly designed to be right at this very moment?

I don't want you to do what so many of us do when we think about weight. We think, "Let me just lose this 15 pounds and I'll be able to get started on that Healthy Voice thing." No. I know that came up for me even writing this book! I thought, "I'll get life figured out when the book is done. Then life kept happening so I just had to get the book done and keep living life!" Life keeps going! So we've got to adjust our sails and adapt. It's funny because my old boss at the White House, Matt Schlapp referred to my Dad once as a "ship that never lets his sails down" and I laughed hysterically, but you know what's funny? I'm not letting my sails down on this. I'm committed to BEING the Healthy Voice for myself so I can be it for you and for the world (no I will not do it to my crazy perfectionist tendencies). I'm committed to the journey of BEING, not fixing myself to get to that place of BEING.

Imagine a map of your body and maybe there is a satellite dropping at one of the four points on your body. One will drop somewhere on your body, another on your head, another on your heart and another on the center of your being. They signify the physical, mental, emotional, and spiritual parts of you. The question is, at which point are you willing to start? If "you are here", what is it you are going to do first to get you into action? Go back to the guide and walk through the steps to meet yourself where you are willing to start. Where have you already started and maybe go from there?

You can start anywhere. You need a transformation and in order to get that, you need to start with a new approach that isn't about the fix, but a journey. We need you to be strong in heart, mind, body and spirit so you can be the Healthy Voice in your life.

If you are willing to change physically, get real about your Food and Fitness Truth. What hasn't worked? What has? What do you really need to do to get grounded so this journey can work? Don't make it about the physical! Remember, that's the tool to get you beyond this. Find the program that works for where you are at right now and be as honest as you possibly can with yourself. No excuses! Get beyond the thinking that this can only be a fitness and nutrition thing and that never worked for you. You know now there is more to it and behavior modification is a huge piece of it. Your Healthy Voice can help you with that navigating triggers and the road ahead! You don't even have to do it alone! What might help you is to journal about where you've been and what you might need now so you can get to where you need to go. Believe me, I know the whole world seems to be stuck in the physical fix. That's why I wrote this book, to get you ahead of the game—so don't get stuck in that thinking! They'll catch up. You know it's going to be tough to do something different than you've always done, but you know in the long run finding something that makes you enjoy working out and not obsesses about food will make your life a whole lot easier. So do your work!

If you are willing to face what's going on with your Unhealthy Voice holding you back, then I commend you. You are brave. If you are realizing that there is some stuff you went through that you know is keeping you physically unhealthy, then awesome—you've made the first step by just getting aware. If you are ready to address your mental health then more power to you. You are not alone in this. Many have gone before you. Again, just like the physical—the world is a little behind on accepting that mental health is an issue, let alone a factor in our weight. So you are ahead of the game if you are taking action on it now. Be patient with yourself. Check things out. The more present you get to it now, the more ready you will be when the guide and the tools come out for you to start really embracing the journey. There are many tools and resources to getting some answers to this stuff. Remember, your mental game plays a huge factor in the physical. If it gets you down, don't let anyone tell you that you can just do it with willpower. Not everyone can!

If you have come into awareness about some behavior that you don't want to be doing, or you've joined a program and stopped doing it—it's the perfect time to start getting aware of the triggers all around you. So write them down in your journal or on your phone because they will help you understand yourself and be a tool to help you navigate life. This is the best time to get to know your triggers. Don't use them as sticks to beat yourself up though. They are tools for the journey to empower your Healthy Voice while you navigate your Unhealthy one! Speaking of your Unhealthy Voice, it can be a very powerful one that will tell you to put down this book and never take another step. That's what it wants you to do, think you can't do it. I've already told you that you can and you already know what you've done, even if you can't physically see the results. If you've gotten through something in your life—you've got the spirit within you to take the first steps.

If you've got a relationship with God that you really love, keep turning to it! If you don't, and this book has sparked your interest—get open to it, and where you find it, because it's all yours. In fact, whatever this journey is teaching you about yourself and how your Healthy Voice speaks to you all around, journal about it because it's going to be like getting to know yourself in a whole new way. Just make sure you are a kind companion to yourself! Finally, if you feel like you don't have the courage or the time to do this, pray for the courage. If that doesn't work, call a friend who gets you, who you know has been through something that could give you the courage to get started. Make them your accountability partner and you may just get moving on the road towards your Healthy Voice. Don't expect it to all happen at once! This is the journey of a lifetime!

In that journal you've got or on your phone, I want you to start making note of the Healthy Voice communities, places, people, songs and all the tools that show up in your life that have a positive influence. If they feel like a Healthy Voice in your life, then jot them down because they will lift you up and make you realize how much you have!

Then on social media, I want you to go be positive. Drop the people that make you nuts and bring out your Unhealthy Voice! Encourage those who need it. Get on Pinterest and get creative with things that lift you up. Create boards that inspire you in a positive Healthy voice way, not in a physical or materialistic way. Bring out your Healthy Voice so others can notice it, and if you find triggers—share them so others can feel in company if they share them too!

Be it for another . . . for the world

You already know the journey isn't just about you. It is so important for you to choose a path and start walking it so that you can be part of the walk, but that's not the end. If this were about me just getting myself all squared away, I'd be stuck in my head for the rest in my life. Not where I want to be. It's about everyone who still needs to get on the road and find their Healthy Voice in whatever way they are willing to get started on the journey.

Share your Physical Transformation Story

There are people who are in desperate need of physical transformation. They are struggling with obesity and its related diseases like hypertension and diabetes. If not, they are close to it. Many have started to do something about it, but too many don't know how to get started. They need your help to get started. They need your story. They need your services or they need you to blaze the trail. They need you to be the light that says, "Let's get you started on the journey." They need to know that you know they are more than just a body and that you are committed to their whole selves, not just their physical selves. They don't need you to fix them. They want you to guide them to change so they can live a better life. They want you to show them the way! Do not judge them by how they look for weight struggles don't show up in how people look. The deeper struggle is how it feels to carry it physically and emotionally. Whoever comes to you, be that Healthy Voice without judgment no matter what size or shape they come because you never know what battle they are fighting on the inside or in their life scenario. Never assume it's about what you see. Just be the Healthy Voice the best way you can with what you have. You just have to be it.

When it comes to the next generation, I don't want any kid to have to turn to food to go through something like their parents' divorce. I don't want any kid who may struggle like I did to not be aware of potential genetic factors. I don't want any child to think that their worth lies in their weight, not in the way God created them to be. There is one girl who holds a very special place in my heart with this. She was about 12 when we met and I had been coaching about a year. A nurse at a local clinic had heard about what I do in working with adults and children to get beyond the weight. Her willingness to work with me astounded me. I'll never forget her first meeting when she said, "Everyone in my class who is overweight is mean and I don't want to be angry about my weight."

Here was an amazingly perceptive young girl who realized her emotions around her weight were getting the best of her. She was also fully aware they were getting the best of the other kids who were also struggling with weight. She saw what she did not want. She wanted a different way. It was a miracle that we met. Her Mom was so great in her willingness to have her daughter go that deeper path so that she could have tools for living instead of just an eating plan. She and I met regularly talking about food at home and school, exercise and eating habits. Addressing some of that allowed us to get to what was underneath that was causing her to turn to that food when she'd get home from school or turn to it when she was feeling sad or lonely. I was amazed at how similar our stories were. Through her, I began to recognize my own self at her age and realized why I ate so much! I also realized why so many more young kids needed this guidance. Each time we met, her Healthy Voice got stronger. She was noticing the things that triggered her in each of her environments. She was able to call it out when the Unhealthy Voice would try to get her down, thereby separating herself from it. Then she was able to really give power to her Healthy Voice in her life. I was amazed to see her transformation in her everyday life. Her smile got bigger with each visit as she told me about the boy she started to like, the basketball team she joined, the grades that went up and her overall attitude about life. It was amazing! Towards the end she said to me, "I want you to come to my school because you are different! Everyone comes to our school to tell us we have to eat good and workout. You teach about 'why' I eat and nobody talks about it like that! You've helped me so much! You need to go to every school!" I was brought to tears realizing how my story, which I kept in for so long, was being used to change this little girls' life. Who knew what else God had planned for reaching more girls like her, but I was up for it!

But these kids aren't just in elementary school. They are in high school and in college. They are at risk for carrying these behaviors into their lives and they need our help to guide them out of that struggle. They are stressed and turning to food, or both food and alcohol and it's having what is probably a similar affect on them as it did with me. If you know kids like this, don't judge them for their outsides! Love them for the person they are inside so they can realize they are more than the weight and be willing to make the change!

Share how you let your Unhealthy Voice Stop Running your Mind

Just like that physical transformation, there are too many people who are struggling with mental illness that goes completely unaddressed. Maybe it's addiction they can't keep under control and are sweeping under the rug. Maybe it's depression or bipolar that they are afraid to treat so they keep it to themselves. Maybe it's an eating disorder that they don't even realize they have that they need to treat, but need help financially or emotionally to get there. Mental illness is REAL. It is not a willpower thing. These people need our help. They need our stories of transformation in getting help for our mental illness. They need to know how we got educated and started to treat it. They need to know where to go to get it treated. Especially when it comes to mental illness, those who struggle the most, cannot leave assessment and treatment up to themselves; they need help. They need us to be the Healthy Voice for them because that is blocking them from the rest of the journey. I know someone named Sonia Lee who is a music artist. I met her in Chicago at a Hazelden Women's conference. She sings about her beautiful recovery journey in a way that is so honest you feel like she is singing to you. She's just one Healthy Voice on the journey of recovery. There are Olympic Athletes and movie stars that make the journey of recovery work. It's not just what you see in the headlines of those who keep falling. There are so many. I've seen Demi Lovato get help for her mental health by going to treatment for her eating disorder and bipolar. She is singing her heart out and reaching girls all over the world with her Healthy Voice. If they can do it, those kids can too.

Share how your Spiritual Journey has brought you Victory!

This can be the hardest to overcome, but there are so many that are just stuck in a battle with this one. It's staggering how many struggle with it and even more how many people keep it to themselves. Getting past it requires walking through it. It requires recognizing those people who have gotten through it with something bigger than life. There are too many people who are going through life with such deep struggle not knowing they don't have to walk it alone. They feel lost and alone and they don't have to. For those of you who don't feel that way, they are waiting to hear your story and share the walk with you. At the deepest level of ourselves, we need this Healthy Voice for our world because so many are stuck on the surface. So many are pretending everything is fine yet absolutely dying on the inside emotionally. That keeps us stuck in our Unhealthy Voice. It doesn't mean we all want to get out of it, but there are many of us that do—and those are the people I know we can reach with the Healthy Voice and the light of the spirit.

What we don't realize is that in our shame, fear, our brokenness, and our inner turmoil, we think we are alone but God is holding us. He's carrying us right through it. Anyone who has gone through or is going through feelings of abandonment through divorce, loss of a loved one, addiction in ourselves or ones we love, physical or emotional abuse, rape, eating disorders, mental illness, or obesity—you get it. We feel so ashamed about these things that we feel we can't share what we went through, but we can. We can find the Healthy Voice in people, places, and communities that will bring us to the place where we realize we are not worthless. There is nothing to be ashamed of. We are enough. In fact, we've always been enough and we are way beyond worthy. We are called. So no matter how far in your emotional struggle you are, you aren't too far. He's got you. Know that. You can lean on Him anytime you want.

"Finally, be strong in the Lord and in his mighty power. Put on the full armor of God, so that you can take your stand against the devil's schemes. For our struggle is not against the flesh and blood, but against the rulers, against

> *the authorities, against the powers of this dark world and against the spiritual forces of evil in the heavenly realms."*
> —*NIV, Ephesians 6:10–12*

I went to the World Pulse Festival in South Bend while I was finishing this book and came home afterward to find that one of the musicians from the show was performing at our church. Her name is Dara Maclean. It was almost a miracle that I'd missed her at the show because I got to experience her powerful presence, actual Healthy voice and inner one in person. It blew me away. I even got to tell her that. She not only sends the message through her lyrics, her voice and her message, but directly through her heart. The light shines out. She knows God's there, and she's singing about it. Her song, "Suitcases", can be found on You Tube or her website www.daramaclean.com.

It's time for you find it, live it, share it, and be it. No matter what you've been through you don't have to be afraid. You ARE a Healthy Voice for the people you love and serve. But you can be an even better one if you recognize the light within you.

ACTION TIME

- It's time to thank God for being there on your journey because that's where the power lies for this new one.
- It's time to turn the shame over to God because it's not serving you anymore.
- It's time to turn your fear of moving forward into one step ahead.
- It's time to turn that weight struggle in your mind and body into victory.
- It's time to call out your addiction and get real about how you can change it.
- It's time to stop comparing or judging and get focused on your own road.

- It's time to stop focusing on your outside and get inside.
- It's time to turn off the excuses and take inspired action.

Why?

- Because you are worth more than your weight, your struggles, your weaknesses and all those things that hold you back.
- Because we need your Healthy Voice AND your awareness of your Unhealthy Voice Triggers so you can inspire others.
- Because you are made for more than the power you've been giving to the food and your weight.
- Because we need your light from every aspect of your story and so do a lot of other people.
- Because we need you to inspire others in ways you don't even know yet or could even imagine.
- Because we're ready for you to move forward despite what your Unhealthy Voice tells you. We know you are willing to get beyond that darkness and take one step forward into the light.

We know that you have that light in you no matter what. This book did not give it to you. You already had it within you. You are worth it. So let's get started. Let's get your light shining my friend!

A Special Call to my Healthy Voice Girls

You guys deserve to walk the journey with tools to live your best life. You guys deserve to live it from the inside out and enjoy every minute, to be in your bodies, free in your minds and spirits. I hope you begin to find that on this path. If you've made any mistakes, you can be real and choose a different path. It's okay. You don't have to do it perfect. You just deserve to treat yourself with love and compassion, because you are totally worth it. If you want that foundation in building a relationship with God who can help you stand tall as you walk, then I'll be by your side. If you want something simpler, then we'll help you find your way. Whatever it is, you don't have to walk the path alone. You get to find hope within you and around you now. You get to find power within you. Go to my website and find out how you can connect to other Healthy Voice Girls like you who are just trying to find their way on the journey. We'd love to have you join our community!

For Businesses, Non-Profits, Service Providers

People finding the Healthy Voice are going to need you to show up. If you are interested in being part of our Healthy Voice Collective where we are bringing people and organizations together fighting for those who need to get beyond the weight go to www.findyourhealthyvoice.com to find out more.

For You, the Reader

Congratulations for making it this far. The beauty is that we're just getting started. That's why I love that this book isn't the fix! It's the journey! That being said, don't forget—this a journey with yourself. You don't have to run from yourself anymore. You are learning to be your own companion through this process. Of course we need an escape sometimes to regroup, but we don't need to run from ourselves. We're always with ourselves. Wherever we go, there we are—as the saying goes. So settle into the journey. Your higher power has given you yourself so you can feel at home in yourself through everything. It doesn't mean you are happy all the time, but you are feeling, growing, learning and healing. You are on the journey, going through the process. You'll have breakthroughs, revelations, and good cries. You have awesome days and tough days. Above all, you know the journey doesn't end. Some days it feels like a marathon. Some days you feel like you've reached a finish line. No matter what, the journey of the Healthy Voice goes on forever. That's a good thing because you never have to worry about getting to the final finish line! What a relief! As my Dad would say, "Isn't this great?"

Remember I'm walking with you. I've got my journey and you've got yours. My Healthy Voice meets me where I am when I need it how I choose it! I don't know where you are at but know that wherever you are is OKAY! That's where your Healthy Voice is ready to meet you. Speaking of that, I can't wait to meet you on the journey and find out how you are all connecting.

> *"Brothers and sisters, I do not consider myself yet to have taken hold of it. But one thing I do: Forgetting what is behind and straining toward what is ahead, I press on toward the goal to win the prize for which God has called me heavenward in Jesus Christ".*
> —*NIV, Philippians 3:13-14*

Just remember we are ALL in this together. Anytime you think you are alone, turn off that voice because it's an Unhealthy Voice! You walk it alone and that is a beautiful thing but you will never have to get through anything alone. Don't minimize your being to just a physical self or a fix! Look at it like a marathon if you need a fitness marathon, but there isn't going to be a finish line for a very long, long time. Get your eyes out of the outcomes. Keep your feet moving. Keep your gaze focused on the horizon. Share with the runners next to you. Be there for the runners next to you. Be there for yourself.

A Final Note

This book was written with a plan to share my story and how I found my Healthy Voice through recovery and behavior modification. I had no idea that my father would die. It drastically slowed down the process of the book production. I realized within days of the loss that it was an opportunity to show you the reader that you can get through absolutely anything if you are willing to go on the journey, rather than the fix, relying on a power greater than yourself. As I write these words, it's about one day to the one full year anniversary of my father's passing. It's been a wild ride. It's also been one where I've literally felt his presence every step of the way. I've learned so much about myself and I feel like I've literally grown up into the woman I'm supposed to be. Every time I've been down, I've been lifted up by the fact that the time has now come for me to carry the light and I'm okay with that. I'm learning to really stand on my own two feet. I know he is shining with pride from above. I know that if I could get through something like this, you can too.

As I finish, it feels like I have to say goodbye to Dad. I know he will be with me on the journey ahead. He will be with me as this book comes alive in my life and yours. I just can't wait to see what happens next. There's a quote I read in the book "Heaven is Real: Lessons on Earthly Joy—What Happened After 90 Minutes in Heaven", it brought me so much comfort I just had to put it right here at the end of the book with an accompanying song.

> *"One day you will read in the paper that I died. Don't believe a word of it: I'll be more alive than ever."*
>
> —*Dwight L. Moody*

The song that brings joy to my heart when I think of heaven is by a band called Building 429 and it's called "Where I Belong". It brings me peace when I miss Dad and when earth is just a rough place to be.

That's my truth. You have yours. We all have our own and we get to walk the journey together!

I'm good with my new normal. I'm happy I've chosen my Healthy Voice. I love that I can find those winks from heaven in my life. I'm so incredibly grateful for every earthly memory we had together. I'm grateful for the healing miracle we had in our relationship. I'm grateful for the continued healing through our spiritual one.

I choose to carry on Dad's legacy of the glass half full. As he would say when he punched you in the arm and he wanted you to notice how great things were, “Isn’t this great?”

Yes Dad. It’s great. Miss You. Can’t wait to see you again. Love you to infinity too.

XOXO

Mere.

I leave you with the quote that’s stuck with me since I found it years ago and a little Healthy Voice Inspiration just to keep you going in case you didn’t get enough!

“What lies behind us, and what lies before us are
tiny matters compared to what lies within us.”
—Ralph Waldo Emerson

References

11. Ogden, Cynthia L. et al. Prevalence of Obesity in the United States, 2009-2010, Centers for Disease Control National Center for Health Statistics, *http://www.cdc.gov/nchs/data/databriefs/db82.pdf.*
12. National Association of Anorexic Nervosa and Associated Disorders, Inc. Eating Disorder Statistics *http://www.anad.org/get-information/about-eating-disorders/eating-disorders-statistics/*
13. Obesity Action Coalition, "Obesity Statistic Fact Sheets", Obesity Action Coalition website. *http://www.obesityaction.org/educational-resources/obesity-statistics-fact-sheets.*
14. American Academy of Child and Adolescent Psychiatry, "Teenagers with Eating Disorders." Fact Sheet. *http://www.aacap.org/cs/root/facts_for_families/teenagers_with_eating_disorders.*
15. Centers for Disease Control and Prevention, "Fact Sheets: Binge Drinking," *http://www.cdc.gov/alcohol/fact-sheets/binge-drinking.htm.*
16. College Binge Drinking.net website, *http://www.collegebingedrinking.net/.*

17. Summers, Nick. "Party Hard, Study Harder," Newsweek Magazine, *http://www.thedailybeast.com/newsweek/2011/09/11/college-study-abroad-programs-get-serious-with-studies.html,* September 11 2011.

18. Cox, Chris. *https://www3.nd.edu/~newsinfo/pdf/2008_04_02_pdf/ND%20researchers%20group%20gives%20local%20binge%20eaters%20a%20way%20out.pdf.* April 2, 2008.

19. Lerner, Marty, PhD. "Basics of Recovery—S.E.R.F." Milestonesprogram.org. *http://www.milestonesprogram.org/news/10/Basics_Of_Recovery___S_E_R_F_.*

20. Martin, Ben. "Fight or Flight", Psychcentral.com. *http://psychcentral.com/lib/2006/fight-or-flight/.*

21. Fedeli, Umberto. Personal communication, June 27, 2012.